FUTURE
English for Results

3

TESTS and TEST PREP
with **Exam**_View_® *Assessment Suite*

Daniel S. Pittaway

Series Consultants

Beatriz B. Díaz

Ronna Magy

Federico Salas-Isnardi

PEARSON
Longman

Future 3 Tests and Test Prep

Pearson Education, 10 Bank Street, White Plains, NY 10606

Staff credits: The people who made up the *Future 3 Tests and Test Prep* team, representing editorial, production, design, and manufacturing, are: Jennifer Adamec, Rhea Banker, Nancy Blodgett, Aerin Csigay, Mindy DePalma, Nancy Flaggman, Irene Frankel, Katherine Keyes, Linda Moser, Barbara Sabella, Julie Schmidt, and Kim Steiner.
Cover design: Rhea Banker
Cover photo: Kathy Lamm/Getty Images
Text composition: TSI Graphics
Text font: Minion Regular
Text design: Barbara Sabella

Photo credits: Page 37 Photolibrary Group; Page 41 (#1) Julianne Bockius Phography/Photographers Direct, (#3) Howard Birnstihl Photography/Photographers Direct, (#5) Zachariah Lindsey Heyer/ istockphoto, (#8) Derrick Alderman/Alamy

Illustration credits: Deborah Crowle, page 6; Brian Hughes, page 2; Allan Moon, pages 30, 58, 65, 81

ISBN-10: 0-13-240882-1
ISBN-13: 9780132408820

PEARSON LONGMAN ON THE WEB

Pearsonlongman.com offers online resources for teachers and students. Access our Companion Websites, our online catalog, and our local offices around the world.

Visit us at **www.pearsonlongman.com**.

Printed in the United States of America
2 3 4 5 6 7 8 9 10 —V012— 14 13 12 11

Contents

Introduction iv

Test Prep viii

   Test-Taking Strategy Worksheets viii

   Sample Unit Test xi

Unit 1 Test 1

Unit 2 Test 8

Unit 3 Test 15

Unit 4 Test 22

Unit 5 Test 29

Unit 6 Test. 36

Unit 7 Test. 43

Unit 8 Test. 50

Unit 9 Test. 57

Unit 10 Test. 64

Unit 11 Test. 71

Unit 12 Test. 79

Answer Sheet. 87

Answer Keys and Audio Scripts 89

Welcome to *Future 3 Tests and Test Prep.* This package (containing a book, an audio CD, and a CD-ROM) provides all the assessment tools you need:

- The **Test Prep** section at the beginning of the book contains test-taking strategy worksheets and a sample unit test. These pages are photocopiable.
- The **Printed Unit Tests** in the book, also photocopiable, test students' mastery of the content presented in the Student Book units. The audio CD accompanies these tests.
- The **Exam***View® Assessment Suite* CD-ROM, found in the same envelope as the audio CD, offers a wealth of additional ways to assess students. Teachers can create their own unique tests or print or customize already prepared unit tests in addition to midterm and final tests.

Test Prep

Test-Taking Strategy Worksheets

Many adult ESL students are unfamiliar with standardized tests. The Test Prep section contains reproducible worksheets that will prepare students for both the printed unit tests in this book and for any standardized tests they may have to take, such as the CASAS Life and Work Series. You will find the following worksheets on pages viii-x:

- How to Use an Answer Sheet
- Practice Questions for Standardized Tests
- Test-Taking Strategies

You can distribute the worksheets to your class over a period of time (for example, one page a week). Alternatively, you can wait until students are close to the time they will be tested or post-tested and then go over all the material in one session.

Sample Unit Test

The Sample Unit Test gives students the opportunity to practice the kinds of questions they will answer in the Unit Tests. On pages xi–xvi you will find:

- Instructions for the Sample Unit Test
- Sample Unit Test (Listening, Life Skills, Grammar, and Vocabulary)
- Answer Key and Audio Script for the Sample Unit Test

To administer the Sample Unit Test:

- Go over the Instructions for the Sample Unit Test with your class.
- Make copies of the test and of the blank Answer Sheet on page 87. Distribute the copies to your students. Have them bubble in their test answers on the Answer Sheet.
- The audio for the sample listening questions can be found on the audio CD, Track 2. There are 10-second pauses after each conversation to allow students to respond to the questions.
- Check answers using the Answer Key and the Audio Script for the Sample Unit Test on page xvi.

The Sample Unit Test (with the exception of the grammar section) is similar in format and content to the CASAS Life and Work Reading and Listening Series tests, but not identical to them. The CASAS website (www.casas.org) offers additional information, such as practice test questions, that you may find useful.

Printed Unit Tests

There are 12 printed Unit Tests in this test book. They are designed to assess how well students have mastered the material presented in each unit of the Student Book. Each test contains the following sections:

- Listening
- Life Skills
- Grammar
- Vocabulary
- Reading

The Listening, Life Skills, Vocabulary, and Reading sections of the tests emulate the look and feel of the CASAS Life and Work Reading and Listening Series tests. All the sections use a multiple-choice format, modeling the format students will encounter in standardized tests.

Listening

The Listening section includes a variety of item types and is divided into three parts: Listening I, Listening II, and Listening III.

Students listen to test items and look at the answer choices on the test page.

In **Listening I**, students hear a short conversation and have to answer a comprehension question about that conversation.

In **Listening II**, students hear part of a short conversation, and they have to choose the appropriate response to continue the conversation.

In **Listening III**, students hear a conversation. They then hear three sentences about the conversation and have to choose which sentence is true.

The directions and the answer choices appear on the Listening test page. This is different from the CASAS test, where students are not given answer choices to look at. In other words, on the CASAS test, students bubble in their answers on the answer sheet, but they do not see the questions or answer choices in print. If your students need extra support, give them the Listening Test page when you distribute the test. But if you wish to emulate CASAS more closely, you should omit this page.

Life Skills

In the Life Skills section, students read a brief text or look at falsalia, such as a sales ad or job application. They then answer comprehension questions about it.

Grammar

Students are asked to complete short conversations that contain examples of the grammar points presented in the unit.

Vocabulary

Students complete sentences. The focus is on vocabulary items that were presented in the vocabulary lesson of the unit.

Reading

Students read a short passage that reflects the grammar and themes covered in the unit and then answer comprehension questions about it.

Answer Keys and Audio Scripts

You will find an Answer Key and an Audio Script for each printed Unit Test at the back of this book. The Answer Key is an answer sheet with the correct answers for the test bubbled in. It also provides diagnostic information about each test question. The Audio Script includes the conversations and comprehension questions. The direction lines and answer choices, which are also recorded, appear only on the test page.

Administering and Scoring Printed Unit Tests

To administer a printed Unit Test:

- Find the test you want in this book and photocopy it.
- Decide whether or not you want students to look at the Listening page as they take the test (see the Listening section). Either include or omit the Listening page when you distribute the test.
- Make copies of the blank Answer Sheet on page 87 and distribute them to your students. Ask students to bubble in their test answers on the Answer Sheet.

- Start with the Listening section of the test. Locate the appropriate audio track on the audio CD. Note that each item of the Listening section has a separate track. We recommend that you play each track twice, pausing for 10 to 20 seconds between each play. This will approximate how listening is presented on standardized tests.
- Each 33-item test is designed to take 25 to 30 minutes to administer.

To score a printed Unit Test:

- Collect your students' bubbled-in Answer Sheets.
- Locate the Answer Key for the test at the back of this book. To create a scoring mask, photocopy the Answer Key and punch a hole in each bubbled-in answer. When you lay this scoring mask over a student's Answer Sheet, you can easily see if the student has bubbled in the correct answer. If the bubble is not filled in, then simply mark an X on the unmarked bubble with a colored pencil.
- Count the number of correctly bubbled-in answers on the student's Answer Sheet. Each correct answer is worth three points. To calculate a percentage score for your students, multiply the number of correct answers by three and add one point.

The Answer Key provides the objective that each item tests, along with the lesson and page number in the Student Book where the material was presented. If a student answers a particular item incorrectly, you will then know which competency the student has missed and/or in which lesson he or she may need further practice.

Exam*View®* *Assessment Suite*

The **Exam***View®* *Assessment Suite* can be used either to supplement the printed Unit Tests or in place of them. With **Exam***View*, you can create or customize your own tests for students. Alternatively, you can choose to simply print out Unit, Midterm, or Final tests that have already been prepared for you and administer them to your class.

For detailed information on how to install the **Exam***View* software and use it to create, customize, and print out tests, please refer to the *TO THE TEACHER* PDF located on the *Future 3* **Exam***View Assessment Suite* CD-ROM. The installation instructions in the back of the book will tell you how to find this document.

Exam*View* Unit Tests

The **Exam***View* unit tests have the same general structure as the printed unit tests in the book, with a series of multiple choice questions that test listening, grammar, vocabulary, life skills, and reading skills. However, the **Exam***View* unit tests do not follow the CASAS testing format as closely as the printed unit tests do. Another difference is that there are two separate types of tests for each unit. The first is a Listening Test in PDF format. The Listening Tests are offered in PDF format to make them easier for teachers to administer. Students listen to longer conversations (similar to the listenings in the Student Book) and then answer comprehension questions about them.

The second type of test is an **Exam***View* Test, containing grammar, vocabulary, life skills, and reading items.

Exam*View* Midterm and Final Tests

The **Exam***View* Midterm and Final Tests provide an objective, standardized way to assess all your students at the halfway point and at the end of the course. The tests have a total of 66 items each. The Midterm tests the content presented in Units 1–6 and the Final covers Units 7–12. As with the Unit Tests, the Listening Midterm and Final Tests are in PDF format, and grammar, vocabulary, life skills, and reading items are in **Exam***View* question banks.

Administering and Scoring Exam*View* Tests

To administer an **Exam***View* Test:

- You can administer **Exam***View* Tests via computer or simply print them out and distribute them to your students. (The Listening Tests, as noted above, can only be administered in print format.)

- Locate the appropriate PDFs and **Exam***View* tests on the CD-ROM. For example, if you wanted to administer the tests for Unit 1, you would print out the Listening test PDF and the **Exam***View* test for Unit 1. (Please refer to the *TO THE TEACHER* PDF for more information on how to select the PDFs or tests you need.)
- Distribute the tests to your students. (Note: the Answer Keys for the **Exam***View* tests print out automatically at the end of the test. Make sure you do not distribute the Answer Key to your students along with the test!)
- If you are printing out tests for your students, make copies of the blank Answer Sheet on page 87. Distribute two copies to each student. One copy is for the Listening Test, and the other copy is for the **Exam***View* Test.
- Start with the Listening Test. Play the appropriate audio tracks for the test. The audio is located on the same CD-ROM as the **Exam***View* software. It can be played on any CD player or computer with CD-playing software. Have students listen and fill in the correct number of bubbles on the first Answer Sheet (usually, for six test items). Then collect the listening answer sheets.
- Next, administer the **Exam***View* test for the unit. Have students bubble in the second Answer Sheet. Collect the Answer Sheets when students are finished.
- Allow 25-30 minutes for students to complete the Listening Test and the **Exam***View* test for each unit. Allow 50-60 minutes for a midterm or final.

To score an **Exam***View* Test:
- Collect your students' bubbled-in Answer Sheets.
- Locate the Answer Keys for the test. The Answer Keys and Audio Script for each Listening test are in PDF format in the same folder as the listening test. The Answer Keys for the **Exam***View* tests will print out automatically at the end of each test, as noted above.
- Count the number of correctly bubbled-in answers on each student's Answer Sheets. Add the scores of the Listening Test and the **Exam***View* test together. Then score the **Exam***View* Unit Tests as you would a printed Unit Test. For the 66-item Midterm or Final test, multiply the number of correct answers by 3, add 2 free points, and divide the result by 2 to get a percentage score.

You can find detailed diagnostic information about each test item in the Answer Keys, including the following:
- Level of difficulty (DIF)
- Reference (REF): Student Book level and unit being tested
- Learning objective (OBJ): the learning objective of the item (as found in the *Scope & Sequence*/Student Book unit lesson)
- National standard (NAT): the CASAS competency being tested, if applicable
- Skill (SKL): the skill being tested (listening, grammar, vocabulary, life skills, or reading)

As with the printed Unit Test Answer Keys, you can use this diagnostic information to determine the competencies and/or lessons in which your students need more practice.

HOW TO USE AN ANSWER SHEET

For many tests, you use an Answer Sheet to mark, or bubble in, your answers. You must use a #2 pencil. You do not mark your answers on the test. A machine may score your answers. The machine reads and records the pencil marks on the Answer Sheet.

First, you need to fill in some personal information on the Answer Sheet.

Here is an example of the Answer Sheet in this book:

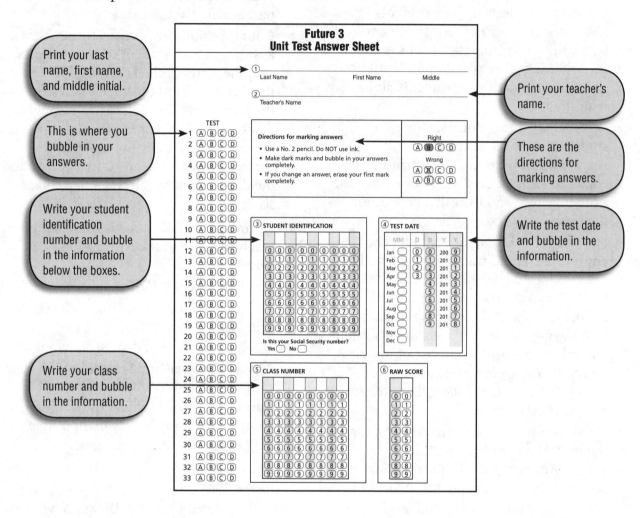

PRACTICE QUESTIONS FOR STANDARDIZED TESTS

Many standardized tests begin with a practice page. Here is an example of a practice page. Read through the questions below and make sure you understand how to answer them.

When you take a standardized test, find the practice page. It says *Practice*. Look for the practice answer box on the answer sheet. Use a pencil. Bubble in your answer. Ask the tester for help if you do not understand the directions. When the test begins, you are not allowed to talk. You cannot ask for or give help.

READING TEST

Practice

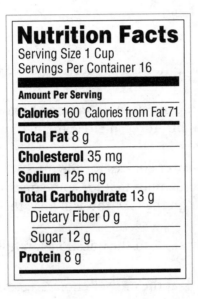

Nutrition Facts
Serving Size 1 Cup
Servings Per Container 16

Amount Per Serving

Calories 160 Calories from Fat 71

Total Fat 8 g

Cholesterol 35 mg

Sodium 125 mg

Total Carbohydrate 13 g

Dietary Fiber 0 g

Sugar 12 g

Protein 8 g

1. How many calories from fat does each serving of this drink have?

A. 1 cup

B. 71

C. 160

D. 8

PRACTICE

1 Ⓐ Ⓑ Ⓒ Ⓓ
2 Ⓐ Ⓑ Ⓒ Ⓓ

TEST-TAKING STRATEGIES

Preparing to Take a Test

- Get a lot of sleep the night before the test.
- Eat a meal or snack before the test.
- Bring two sharpened #2 pencils.
- Bring a pencil eraser.
- Bring a ruler or a blank piece of paper.
- Arrive early to the testing room.
- Make sure you can easily see and hear the tester.
- Turn off your cell phone.
- Try to relax and do your best! Good luck!

Taking a Test

- As soon as you start a test section, look through the section to see how many questions there are.
- Don't spend too much time on any one question. If you don't know the answer, guess and then move on to the next item. You can circle the item number and come back to it at the end if you have time.
- For a listening section: Look at the answer choices for the question. Then listen to the directions and the question. Remember that for some questions, both questions and answer choices may be on the CD. You will hear the questions and the answer choices.
- For all other sections: Read the material. Read the question carefully. Read all the answer choices.
- Think: Which is the best answer? Look at the answer choices again. Eliminate answers you know are not correct.
- Choose the best answer.
- Make sure you mark your answer on the correct line on the answer sheet. Use a ruler to help you, or use a blank piece of paper to cover the lines below the line you are working on.
- Check each time that you bubble in the circle on the correct line for the question you are answering.
- Do not change the first answer you mark unless you are sure that it is wrong.
- Erase completely any answers you have changed. Fill in only ONE answer on each line. Erase all extra marks on your answer sheet.
- When you finish, if there is time, always recheck your answers.
- If you cannot answer many questions, it is OK. Raise your hand. Tell the tester. You may be excused from taking the rest of the test.

INSTRUCTIONS FOR THE SAMPLE UNIT TEST

This sample test is like the Unit Tests in this book. It has Listening, Life Skills, Grammar, and Vocabulary questions. Follow the directions carefully.

Listening Section

All the questions in the Listening section have three answer choices. Here are examples of the three types of listening questions:

Listening I: You listen to a conversation and choose the correct answer to a question about it. You will hear the question both before and after the conversation.

You will hear: What does the woman want to do?

    F: *I need to make an appointment with Dr. Chang.*
    M: *OK. When would you like to come in?*
    F: *Can I come in next Tuesday morning?*

    What does the woman want to do?

    A. She wants to see the doctor on Tuesday.
    B. She wants a job at a doctor's office.
    C. She wants to cancel an appointment.

The correct answer is A.

Listening II: You listen to the first part of a conversation and choose what the person will say next.

You will hear: **F:** *Want to go to the movies tonight?*
    M: *Sorry. I have to work late tonight.*

    A. OK. Let's meet at 6:00.
    B. That's a really good movie.
    C. Too bad. How about tomorrow night?

The correct answer is C.

Listening III: You listen to a conversation and choose which sentence about it is true.

You will hear: **F:** *When did you start working at Al's Electronics?*
    M: *Three years ago. I worked one year as a stock clerk and then I became a sales assistant.*

    Which sentence is true?

    A. The man worked in an electronics store for one year.
    B. The man was a stock clerk before he was a sales assistant.
    C. The man is working as a stock clerk now.

The correct answer is B.

Life Skills Section

The questions in the Life Skills sections have four answer choices. You read a short piece of information, such as a form, label, or map. You then answer questions about the information.

Grammar Section

The questions in the Grammar section have three answer choices. You read a short conversation and choose the correct answer to complete the conversation.

Vocabulary Section

The questions in the Vocabulary section have four answer choices. You choose the correct word or phrase to complete a sentence.

SAMPLE UNIT TEST

💿 LISTENING I

(Track 2) **You will hear a question. Then you will hear a conversation. After that, you will hear the question again and three choices. What is the correct answer: A, B, or C?**

1.   A. He has a headache and a rash.

   B. He has a cough and a stuffy nose.

   C. He has a fever and a sore throat.

💿 LISTENING II

You will hear the first part of a conversation. To finish the conversation, listen and choose the correct answer: A, B, or C.

2.   A. It's great. I'm learning a lot.

   B. I don't think so.

   C. I can't go tonight, but I can go tomorrow night.

💿 LISTENING III

You will hear a conversation. Then you will hear three sentences. Which sentence is true: A, B, or C?

3.   A. Marta is doing very well in all her classes.

   B. Marta is doing best in science.

   C. Marta is having trouble in science and math.

LIFE SKILLS

Read. What is the correct answer: A, B, C, or D?

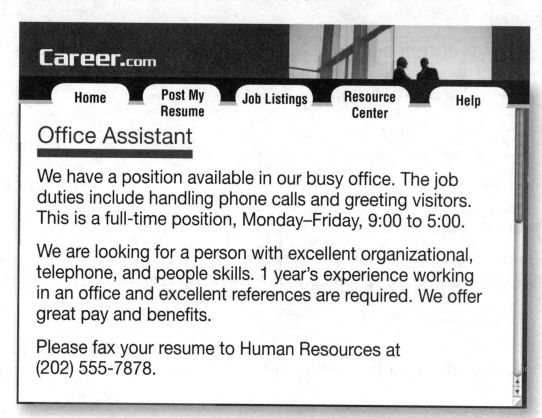

Career.com

| Home | Post My Resume | Job Listings | Resource Center | Help |

Office Assistant

We have a position available in our busy office. The job duties include handling phone calls and greeting visitors. This is a full-time position, Monday–Friday, 9:00 to 5:00.

We are looking for a person with excellent organizational, telephone, and people skills. 1 year's experience working in an office and excellent references are required. We offer great pay and benefits.

Please fax your resume to Human Resources at (202) 555-7878.

4. What is one skill the job applicant must have?

   A. one year of experience

   B. telephone skills

   C. excellent references

   D. a fax machine

5. How many hours a week is the job?

   A. 20 hours

   B. 25 hours

   C. 30 hours

   D. 40 hours

GRAMMAR

Complete each conversation. What is the correct answer: A, B, or C?

6. **A:** _____ borrow your pen for a minute?
   B: Sure. No problem.

   A. Can't I
   B. Could I
   C. Can you

7. **A:** I'm really busy these days.
   B: Me, too. I have _____ work to do.

   A. a lot
   B. many
   C. a lot of

VOCABULARY

Read. What is the correct answer: A, B, C, or D?

8. Employees must _____ at the start of their shift and at the end of each break.

   A. clock in
   B. clock out
   C. call in late
   D. ask questions

9. Please _____ on the shelves when you have finished using it.

   A. report problems
   B. maintain the equipment
   C. wear safety gear
   D. store the equipment

ANSWER KEY AND AUDIO SCRIPT FOR THE SAMPLE UNIT TEST

Answer Key

1. C	4. B	7. C
2. A	5. D	8. A
3. B	6. B	9. D

Audio Script *(Track 2)*

🖸 LISTENING I

1. What are the child's symptoms?

   M: Hello. Metro Clinic.

   F: Hi. I need to make an appointment for my son. His throat is sore and he has a fever. He says it hurts when he swallows.

   M: I see. And does he have a rash?

   F: No, no rash... When can I bring him in?

   What are the child's symptoms?

🖸 LISTENING II

2. **M:** I don't have to work tonight. Do you want to go out to eat?

   F: Sorry, I can't. I have class tonight.

   M: Oh, yeah. How *is* your class?

🖸 LISTENING III

3. **F:** Hi, Mr. Vega. I'm Marta's teacher, Linda Eng.

   M: Nice to meet you. So, how's Marta doing in your class?

   F: Marta is a good student. She works hard in math and science. She does very well in those classes, science especially.

   M: That's great. What about English and history?

   F: Well, she's having a little trouble in those classes. She needs to work on her reading skills.

   Which sentence is true?

Unit 1 Test

🔘 LISTENING I

(Tracks 3-4) **You will hear a question. Then you will hear a conversation. After that, you will hear the question again and three choices. What is the correct answer: A, B, or C?**

1. A. She goes to a parade at the park.
    B. She watches fireworks.
    C. She goes to a barbecue at her friend's house.

2. A. He goes swimming at the beach.
    B. He plays soccer with his friends.
    C. He plays basketball with his friends.

🔘 LISTENING II

(Tracks 5-6) **You will hear the first part of a conversation. To finish the conversation, listen and choose the correct answer: A, B, or C.**

3. A. That's great. I'm off on Friday.
    B. Well, I used to, but my schedule changed.
    C. We used to go to the movies all the time.

4. A. I used to, but now I just want to stay home with my kids.
    B. I'm going to a party for New Year's Eve.
    C. New Year's Eve used to be my favorite holiday.

🔘 LISTENING III

(Tracks 7-8) **You will hear a conversation. Then you will hear three sentences. Which sentence is true: A, B, or C?**

5. A. The woman lives in Central City.
    B. The man lives near school.
    C. The man lives far from school.

6. A. The man plays soccer on Sundays.
    B. The woman plays soccer on Saturdays.
    C. The woman plays soccer on Sundays.

LIFE SKILLS

Read. What is the correct answer: A, B, C, or D?

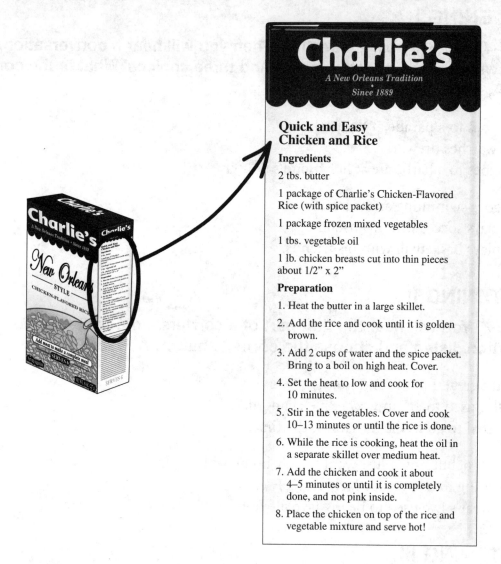

Charlie's
A New Orleans Tradition
Since 1889

Quick and Easy Chicken and Rice

Ingredients

2 tbs. butter

1 package of Charlie's Chicken-Flavored Rice (with spice packet)

1 package frozen mixed vegetables

1 tbs. vegetable oil

1 lb. chicken breasts cut into thin pieces about 1/2" x 2"

Preparation

1. Heat the butter in a large skillet.

2. Add the rice and cook until it is golden brown.

3. Add 2 cups of water and the spice packet. Bring to a boil on high heat. Cover.

4. Set the heat to low and cook for 10 minutes.

5. Stir in the vegetables. Cover and cook 10–13 minutes or until the rice is done.

6. While the rice is cooking, heat the oil in a separate skillet over medium heat.

7. Add the chicken and cook it about 4–5 minutes or until it is completely done, and not pink inside.

8. Place the chicken on top of the rice and vegetable mixture and serve hot!

7. You need _____ of butter.

A. 1 tablespoon

B. 2 tablespoons

C. 1/2 tablespoon

D. 2 cups

8. Add the water and spice packet _____ the rice is golden brown.

A. until

B. after

C. before

D. unless

9. Add the vegetables. Keep the heat on _____.

A. low

B. medium

C. high

D. boiling

10. Cook the chicken for _____ minutes.

A. 2–3

B. 4–5

C. exactly 10

D. 10–13

GRAMMAR

Complete each conversation. What is the correct answer: A, B, or C?

11. **A:** What _____ you do in your spare time?
    B: I like to play chess.

    A. are
    B. do
    C. does

12. **A:** Your brother is so tall. Does he play basketball?
    B: No, he _____. But he likes to watch it!

    A. does
    B. don't
    C. doesn't

13. **A:** My parents _____ to barbecue on the weekends.
    B: That sounds like a lot of fun.

    A. like
    B. likes
    C. liking

14. **A:** _____ do you play football?
    B: At the high school.

    A. How often
    B. Who
    C. Where

15. **A:** That's a really beautiful guitar. Who _____ it?
    B: My sister.

    A. play
    B. plays
    C. playing

16. A: Do we have any fruit?

    B: I think there are _____ apples in the bowl.

        A. a little

        B. a few

        C. any

17. A: Is there any juice in the fridge?

    B: Oh, I'm sorry. There isn't _____ left.

        A. any

        B. some

        C. a few

18. A: There isn't _____ milk left.

    B: But I think there's enough for my coffee.

        A. a little

        B. several

        C. much

19. A: We ate almost everything!

    B: I know. There is only _____ rice left!

        A. a few

        B. a little

        C. any

20. A: We don't have a lot of water.

    B: How _____ bottles do we have?

        A. any

        B. much

        C. many

21. **A:** Look at this old picture! Is that you dancing?

   B: Yeah, I _____ a good dancer.

   A. use to

   B. use to be

   C. used to be

22. **A:** Do you ride a motorcycle?

   B: I _____, but I don't anymore.

   A. used

   B. used to

   C. use to

23. **A:** What do you miss about your home country?

   B: I miss the beach. I _____ every day.

   A. use to swim

   B. used to swim

   C. used swim

24. **A:** Do you miss your mother's cooking?

   B: Yes, I really do. She _____ a big meal every Sunday in Ecuador.

   A. used to cook

   B. used to

   C. cooks

25. **A:** My family _____ go to the park every Friday.

   B: Mine too!

   A. used to be

   B. used to

   C. used

VOCABULARY

Read. What is the correct answer: A, B, C, or D?

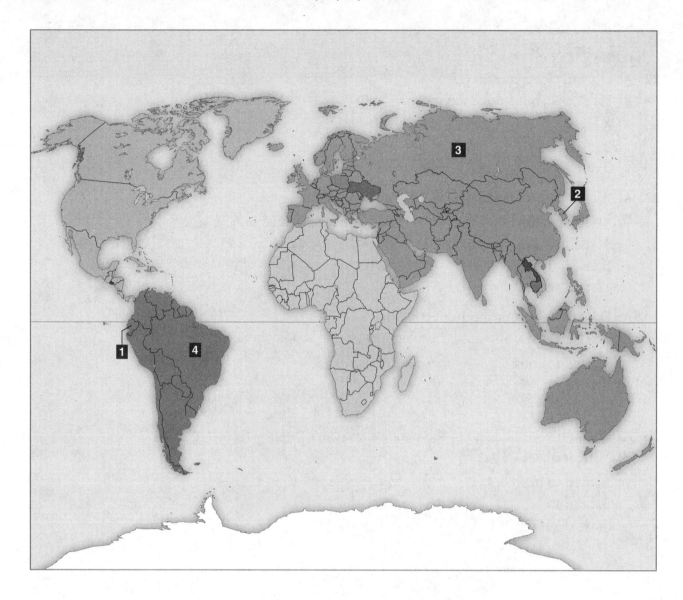

26. What country is number 1?

    A. Russia

    B. Ecuador

    C. Brazil

    D. Korea

27. What country is number 2?

    A. Russia

    B. Ecuador

    C. Brazil

    D. Korea

28. What country is number 3?

    A. Russia

    B. Ecuador

    C. Brazil

    D. Korea

29. What language do people speak in number 4?

    A. Russian

    B. Spanish

    C. Portuguese

    D. Korean

READING

Read. What is the correct answer: A, B, C, or D?

The Garcia family is from Jalisco, Mexico. Their life there was difficult. Mr. Garcia was a police officer, but he wasn't able to make enough money for them to live on. Mrs. Garcia couldn't find work. They knew they could have a better life in the United States. Last year they decided to move to Austin, Texas.

It wasn't easy at first. For the first few months, Mr. Garcia didn't have a job. But now he is working as a security guard. He likes his new job. And he also enjoys his time off. He has friends at work who are also from Jalisco. They get together on the weekends and cook food together. They also watch their favorite soccer teams on TV.

Mrs. Garcia's life has improved also. At first she needed an interpreter for her son's parent-teacher conferences. But now Mrs. Garcia can speak to her son's teachers. She takes an English class at the adult school near her home, and she practices English every day. Now she's ready to look for a job. Maybe she'll find a job at the market down the street from their apartment!

---

30. What is the main idea of the article?

A. The Garcia family is from Jalisco, Mexico.

B. The Garcia family moved to the United States.

C. The Garcia family moved to improve their quality of life.

D. Mr. Garcia is a security guard.

31. What was the problem?

A. Mrs. Garcia couldn't get a job.

B. Mrs. Garcia wanted to stay in Mexico.

C. The quality of life in Texas was not good.

D. They couldn't earn enough money.

32. What did Mr. Garcia use to be?

A. He used to be a security guard.

B. He used to be a police officer.

C. He used to be a student.

D. He used to be a teacher.

33. What's the main idea of the last paragraph?

A. Mrs. Garcia's English has improved.

B. Mrs. Garcia wants to get a job.

C. Mrs. Garcia's life has improved.

D. Mrs. Garcia wants to work at the supermarket near her house.

Unit 2 Test

🔘 LISTENING I

(Tracks 9-10) You will hear a question. Then you will hear a conversation. After that, you will hear the question again and three choices. What is the correct answer: A, B, or C?

1. A. take night classes in the summer
   B. start working the night shift at the college
   C. enroll in classes at Cedar Falls Community College

2. A. a certificate
   B. an associate's degree
   C. a job

🔘 LISTENING II

(Tracks 11-12) You will hear the first part of a conversation. To finish the conversation, listen and choose the correct answer: A, B, or C.

3. A. That's OK. I need to make more money.
   B. Thanks, but I like my job.
   C. Thanks. I'll start looking tomorrow.

4. A. Oh, so you want a job with a different schedule.
   B. That's great!
   C. It's a good idea to work nights.

🔘 LISTENING III

(Tracks 13-14) You will hear a conversation. Then you will hear three sentences. Which sentence is true: A, B, or C?

5. A. The woman is not going to go to the meeting.
   B. The woman will definitely go to the meeting.
   C. The woman might go to the meeting.

6. A. The man isn't going to be at the meeting.
   B. The man is going to be at the meeting.
   C. The man might go to the meeting.

LIFE SKILLS

Read. What is the correct answer: A, B, C, or D?

Elena is from Mexico. In the morning, she studies English at an adult school. In the afternoon, she works as a child care aide at an elementary school. After that, she comes home to make dinner for her family. Elena enjoys her work, and it helps to pay the bills. When she knows more English, she hopes to be a teacher's assistant. In the future, she wants to be an elementary school teacher. Her husband works as a waiter in a restaurant. He wants to help his wife become a teacher. They practice English together.

---

7. What is Elena's long-term goal?

A. to learn English

B. to be a child care aide

C. to help to pay the bills

D. to be a teacher

8. What kind of goal is becoming a teacher?

A. a job goal

B. a family goal

C. a community goal

D. a school goal

9. What is one of Elena's short-term goals?

A. to be an elementary school teacher

B. to be a teacher's assistant

C. to volunteer at a school

D. to work as a waiter

10. Which of the following is a support for Elena's goal of becoming a teacher?

A. Elena needs to learn English.

B. She wants to be a teacher.

C. Her husband practices English with her.

D. Elena has two children.

GRAMMAR

Complete each conversation. What is the correct answer: A, B, or C?

11. **A:** I'm going to take some courses at the community college this winter.
    B: That's great. What _____ you study?

    A. will
    B. might
    C. will probably

12. **A:** Will you continue to work after you start school?
    B: Yes, I _____. I'll go to school at night so I can keep my job.

    A. 'll
    B. will
    C. probably

13. **A:** What is your daughter going to study?
    B: She isn't sure. She _____ computer science.

    A. might study
    B. study
    C. will study

14. **A:** How is Miguel going to pay for school?
    B: He's going to work part-time, and he _____ some financial aid. He applied for financial aid, and he's waiting to hear back.

    A. 'll probably
    B. 'll get
    C. 'll probably get

15. **A:** Will there be classes next Monday?
    B: No, it's a national holiday, so we _____ have classes that day.

    A. will probably not
    B. won't
    C. might not

16. A: Are you going to look for a job online?

    B: Yes, _____.

      A. I am

      B. I'm not

      C. I'm

17. A: Do you like your job?

    B: No, I _____ to look for a new one.

      A. going

      B. 's going

      C. 'm going

18. A: My job _____ end next week.

    B: What will you do next?

      A. is going to

      B. going to

      C. are going to

19. A: Lucy and I _____ to go to the job placement center tomorrow.

    B: Great! Can I come with you?

      A. going

      B. are going

      C. is going

20. A: _____ Marta going to look in the classified ads?

    B: Probably. She's also going to look online.

      A. Where

      B. Are

      C. Is

21. **A:** What are you doing this weekend?
    B: I _____ with the community clean-up project.

    A. 'm helping
    B. 're helping
    C. helping

22. **A:** _____ volunteering on Saturday?
    B: Yes, she is.

    A. Will she
    B. Is she
    C. Is she going to

23. **A:** _____ cooking classes next semester?
    B: Yes, I am.

    A. Are you taking
    B. Is she taking
    C. Are we taking

24. **A:** _____ with the food drive next Wednesday?
    B: Sorry, I can't. I have to work that day.

    A. Do you help
    B. Are you going
    C. Are you helping

25. **A:** Is the Community Center going to offer babysitting tomorrow?
    B: Yes, the center _____ free babysitting from 4:00 to 8:00 P.M. tomorrow.

    A. are offering
    B. is offering
    C. offering

VOCABULARY

Read about Tiffany. What is the correct answer: A, B, C, or D?

26. Tiffany is going to _____ because she needs money to pay for her classes.

    A. get a certificate

    B. volunteer at the community center

    C. apply for financial aid

    D. enroll in college

27. She is also going to _____ on Saturdays to make new friends and get some experience working with other people.

    A. register for citizenship classes

    B. get a degree

    C. apply for financial aid

    D. volunteer at the community center

28. Tiffany's goal is to _____ in accounting. She wants to get it in five years.

    A. take citizenship classes

    B. apply for financial aid

    C. get a degree

    D. register for the semester

29. Before she gets her degree, Tiffany is going to _____ in basic accounting.

    A. get a promotion

    B. get a certificate

    C. take citizenship classes

    D. apply for financial aid

READING

Read. What is the correct answer: A, B, C, or D?

One Immigrant's Dream

Sun-Ok loves children. When she lived in Korea, she managed a daycare center for children whose parents worked late into the evening. Now that she lives in Los Angeles, she wants to follow her dream to open her own daycare center. She is planning to register for early childhood education classes at the local community college. She is also going to sign up for English conversation classes at night. Sun-Ok says, "I want to make sure I can talk with the parents. So it's important for me to learn as much English as possible."

Sun-Ok is also reading books about business. She learned that successful business owners set goals. While her long-term goal is to open her business, her short-term goals include saving money for equipment and supplies she will need, continuing her education, and reading at least one book per month about how to run a successful business.

---

30. What is the main idea of the first paragraph?

   A. Sun-Ok managed a daycare center in Korea because she loves children.

   B. The local community college offers the courses Sun-Ok needs, and she is going to take classes there.

   C. Sun-Ok loves children and plans to fulfill her dream of opening her own daycare center.

   D. Sun-Ok wants to learn English better, so she is going to take an English conversation class.

31. Why does Sun-Ok want to take English classes?

   A. so she can register for Early Childhood Education classes

   B. so she can write letters

   C. so she can go to college

   D. so she can speak with parents

32. What is the main idea of the second paragraph?

   A. Reading business books is useful.

   B. Successful business owners set goals.

   C. Saving money is important.

   D. Sun-OK needs to buy equipment and supplies.

33. Which of these is not one of Sun-Ok's short-term goals?

   A. saving money

   B. continuing her education

   C. writing letters to parents

   D. reading books about business

Unit 3 Test

💿 LISTENING I

(Tracks 15-16) **You will hear a question. Then you will hear a conversation. After that, you will hear the question again and three choices. What is the correct answer: A, B, or C?**

1. A. go to bed
    B. do his homework
    C. watch TV

2. A. She doesn't like school.
    B. She has a lot of homework.
    C. A bully hit her at school.

💿 LISTENING II

(Tracks 17-18) **You will hear the first part of a conversation. To finish the conversation, listen and choose the correct answer: A, B, or C.**

3. A. We're good friends.
    B. I ate a sandwich for lunch.
    C. He doesn't like me.

4. A. What did his teacher say?
    B. Yes, please call her.
    C. Oh, I'm glad he's having fun.

💿 LISTENING III

(Tracks 19-20) **You will hear a conversation. Then you will hear three sentences. Which sentence is true: A, B, or C?**

5. A. The man knows what classes his son should take.
    B. The woman tells the man to talk to the counselor.
    C. The woman is a counselor.

6. A. The daughter is not doing well in math.
    B. The daughter likes math.
    C. The daughter wants to study at the learning center.

NAME_____

LIFE SKILLS

Look at the report card. Then answer the questions. What is the correct answer: A, B, C, or D?

Randolph High School Report Card

Student: Cassandra Rivas   Year: 2010–2011

Class	Teacher	Q 1	Q 2	Q 3	Q 4	Final	Comments
Art	Utley	A					Good student.
English	Jacobs	B+					Good student but missed a test.
Algebra 2	Rivera	C					Does not complete all assignments.
Spanish	Rodriguez	A					Excellent student.
Chemistry	Anderson	B–					Needs to pay more attention in class.

Grades

A+	A	B+	B	C+	C	D	F
95–100%	90–94%	85–89%	80–84%	75–79%	70–74%	65–69%	Below 65%

7. In which classes does Cassandra need to work harder?

   A. Art, English, and Spanish
   B. Algebra 2 and Chemistry
   C. Art and Spanish
   D. Algebra 2, English, and Art

8. In which class did Cassandra miss a test?

   A. Art
   B. Algebra 2
   C. Spanish
   D. English

9. In which class does Cassandra need to listen more?

   A. Spanish
   B. English
   C. Chemistry
   D. Algebra 2

10. In which classes is Cassandra doing very well?

   A. Art and English
   B. Spanish and Chemistry
   C. Art and Spanish
   D. English and Chemistry

GRAMMAR

Complete each conversation. What is the correct answer: A, B, or C?

11. **A:** I don't understand my homework.
    B: Then let's go _____ together.

    A. it over
    B. over it
    C. over

12. **A:** Could I see your homework?
    B: Sorry, I already handed _____.

    A. in
    B. in it
    C. it in

13. **A:** Are you going to join the basketball team?
    B: Yes, I'm going to sign _____ tomorrow.

    A. it up
    B. up
    C. up it

14. **A:** Schoolchildren are often not nice to new students.
    B: I know. They _____. And it makes them feel so bad.

    A. make them fun
    B. make it fun
    C. make fun of them

15. **A:** How are you doing with your math homework?
    B: Not bad, but this problem is difficult. Could you help me figure _____?

    A. out
    B. it out
    C. out it

16. **A:** What happened?
    B: Another student _____ my money.

    A. was taken
    B. taking
    C. took

17. **A:** Where _____ you?
    B: On the playground.

    A. was
    B. were
    C. did

18. **A:** _____ you tell anyone?
    B: Yes, I did.

    A. Did
    B. Were
    C. Do

19. **A:** _____ you tell?
    B: My teacher.

    A. What did
    B. Who does
    C. Who did

20. **A:** _____ this happen?
    B: After school.

    A. When did
    B. Where did
    C. What did

21. **A:** Julia is having trouble with math. _____ talk to her teacher?

　　B: That's probably a good idea. Maybe he can give her some extra help.

　　　A. Do I have to
　　　B. Should I
　　　C. Do I

22. **A:** _____ I have to take a science class?

　　B: Yes. You need to take biology this year.

　　　A. Do
　　　B. Does
　　　C. Should

23. **A:** Should I wait to register for classes?

　　B: No, you _____. In fact, today is the last day, so do it right away.

　　　A. should
　　　B. shouldn't
　　　C. don't have to

24. **A:** _____ take three years of English?

　　B: Yes, he does.

　　　A. Does he have to
　　　B. Has he
　　　C. Should he

25. **A:** Should I visit the principal?

　　B: Well, you can if you want to, but you _____. It's enough to call.

　　　A. shouldn't
　　　B. should
　　　C. don't have to

VOCABULARY

Read. What is the correct answer: A, B, C, or D?

26. Janice missed a test yesterday. Today she is going to _____.
    A. help her out
    B. make it up
    C. figure out an answer
    D. do research

27. Anthony is good at math. He is going to _____ with other students after class.
    A. go over the homework
    B. make up the homework
    C. hand in the homework
    D. look up the homework

28. Mrs. Salazar wants to _____ to talk about her daughter.
    A. hand in homework
    B. do research
    C. go to a parent-teacher conference
    D. make up a test

29. Many students like to _____ to do research. The Internet has a lot of information!
    A. go online
    B. make it up
    C. look up a word in a dictionary
    D. hand in homework

READING

Read. What is the correct answer: A, B, C, or D?

Helping Kids After School

Jeffrey wanted to make a difference in his community. He wanted to help kids learn to enjoy school, and he wanted to help them build self-confidence. One day, he saw an ad in the newspaper for after-school tutors. He called the number. A week later, Jeffrey was tutoring middle-school students in a community center near his home in Anaheim, California.

Every Tuesday and Thursday, seventh and eighth grade kids come to the community center to work with Jeffrey and the other tutors. Jeffrey likes to help kids with math. He says, "I always had trouble with math when I was younger, so I can understand the problems they have." He always tries to find out the biggest problem areas for students so he can help them. "When I meet a new student, that's the best part of my day," says Jeffrey.

---

30. What is the main idea of the reading?

A. Jeffrey saw an ad in the newspaper.

B. Every Tuesday and Thursday, Jeffrey tutors seventh and eighth grade kids.

C. Jeffrey wanted to help his community, so he became a tutor.

D. Jeffrey had trouble with math when he was a student.

31. How does Jeffrey want to help the kids?

A. He wants to teach them math.

B. He wants to give them a reason to enjoy school.

C. He wants to improve their self-confidence.

D. A, B, and C

32. Which of the following is true?

A. Jeffrey works with students of all ages.

B. Jeffrey tutors two days a week.

C. Jeffrey was a great math student when he was younger.

D. Jeffrey got his tutoring job through a friend.

33. Which of the following is not true?

A. Jeffrey is the only tutor at the community center.

B. Jeffrey is good at math now.

C. Jeffrey's students have problems with math.

D. Jeffrey tutors students near his home.

Unit 4 Test

💿 LISTENING I

(Tracks 21-22) **You will hear a question. Then you will hear a conversation. After that, you will hear the question again and three choices. What is the correct answer: A, B, or C?**

1. A. two years
   B. three years
   C. five years

2. A. at a bank
   B. at a store
   C. at a restaurant

💿 LISTENING II

(Tracks 23-24) **You will hear the first part of a conversation. To finish the conversation, listen and choose the correct answer: A, B, or C.**

3. A. No, I haven't.
   B. I like to drive.
   C. Three years.

4. A. My boss is great.
   B. I'd like to work for a bigger restaurant.
   C. I work well with others.

💿 LISTENING III

(Tracks 25-26) **You will hear a conversation. Then you will hear three sentences. Which sentence is true: A, B, or C?**

5. A. A family member told the woman about the job.
   B. The woman didn't find the job on the Internet.
   C. A friend told the woman about the job.

6. A. The boss is polite.
   B. The boss is not polite.
   C. The woman is not polite.

LIFE SKILLS

Read the job application. Then answer the questions. What is the correct answer: A, B, C, or D?

CHUCK'S DINER
APPLICATION FOR EMPLOYMENT
PLEASE PRINT CLEARLY

NAME	ADDRESS	PHONE
Gonzalez, Roberto	181 Cedar Street Fullerton, CA 92832	(323) 555-7453

If hired, can you show proof of eligibility to work in the U.S. within 3 days of hiring? ☒ YES ☐ NO

Are you 18 years of age or older? ☒ YES ☐ NO

POSITION APPLYING FOR: Restaurant Waiter   ☐ FT ☒ PT

AVAILABILITY: ☒ M–F DAY ☐ M–F EVE. ☐ WEEKENDS

Have you ever been fired from a job? ☐ YES ☒ NO   IF YES, what was the reason?

EDUCATION	NAME/ADDRESS	GRADUATED YES/NO	DIPLOMA OR DEGREE	YEAR	MAJOR
COLLEGE	Fullerton College Fullerton, CA	No	No		NA
HIGH SCHOOL	Escuela Secundaria Mixta No. 44 Jalisco, Mexico	Yes	Yes	2004	NA

7. Roberto is looking for a(n) _____ job.
   A. weekends-only
   B. evenings-only
   C. part-time
   D. full-time

8. Roberto wants to be a _____.
   A. cook
   B. cashier
   C. waiter
   D. manager

9. Roberto is available to work _____.
   A. Monday and Friday during the day
   B. Monday through Friday in the evening
   C. Monday through Friday during the day
   D. Monday and Friday in the evening

10. Roberto has _____.
   A. a college degree
   B. a high school diploma
   C. a certificate
   D. a major

GRAMMAR

Complete each conversation. What is the correct answer: A, B, or C?

11. **A:** _____ Roberto ever worked on weekends?
    B: Yes, he has.

    A. Has
    B. Did
    C. Had

12. **A:** Have you ever _____ a van?
    B: No, I haven't.

    A. drove
    B. drives
    C. driven

13. **A:** _____ Martin and Rebecca ever answered phones for a business?
    B: I'm not sure. You'll have to ask them.

    A. Have
    B. Has
    C. Having

14. **A:** Has she ever _____ fired?
    B: No, she hasn't.

    A. was
    B. being
    C. been

15. **A:** Have you ever used a fax machine?
    B: Yes, _____.

    A. I have
    B. I haven't
    C. I've

16. **A:** How long has Sarah been a caterer?
  B: She _____ been a caterer for three years.

    A. had
    B. has
    C. have

17. **A:** I _____ in Tucson since 2005.
  B: No kidding? Me too!

    A. have lived
    B. has lived
    C. lived

18. **A:** How long have both of you worked at the hospital?
  B: We _____ here since April.

    A. had been working
    B. has worked
    C. have worked

19. **A:** How long have you been an assistant manager?
  B: I have been an assistant manager _____ 2007.

    A. for
    B. since
    C. in

20. **A:** How long have you lived in this area?
  B: I have lived here _____ two years.

    A. since
    B. from
    C. for

21. **A:** Should I talk to my boss about the problem?
    B: Yes, it _____ you to talk to her.

    A. 's a good idea for
    B. 's a good idea to
    C. was a good idea of

22. **A:** _____ important to be on time.
    B: I know. I'll be punctual from now on.

    A. There's
    B. It's
    C. Is

23. **A:** You got the job! Congratulations!
    B: Thanks. It _____ go to that interview. I'm glad I did!

    A. was difficult for
    B. was difficult for me to
    C. was difficult for me

24. **A:** I need some time off. What should I do?
    B: It's a good idea _____ to your boss.

    A. for you talk
    B. you talk
    C. for you to talk

25. **A:** Sometimes I can't understand my boss.
    B: It's important _____ you to ask questions to make sure you understand.

    A. for
    B. to
    C. of

VOCABULARY

Read. What is the correct answer: A, B, C, or D?

26. Marisa is very _____. She likes to put everything on her desk in its place.

A. hardworking

B. punctual

C. pleasant

D. organized

27. Tomas is very _____. He is never late for work.

A. organized

B. punctual

C. hardworking

D. cooperative

28. Dae-Jung is _____. He is fast and doesn't make mistakes.

A. pleasant

B. cooperative

C. efficient

D. motivated

29. Javier is very nice to customers. He is always _____.

A. punctual

B. efficient

C. dependable

D. pleasant

READING

Read. What is the correct answer: A, B, C, or D?

To Whom It May Concern:

This is a letter of recommendation for Julio Salazar, who is applying for a
job as chef at your restaurant, the Beef House. I have known Julio for five
years. In that time he has been an outstanding employee. He is very
creative, hardworking, dependable, and good with co-workers. He started
as a line cook and was promoted to head chef two years ago. He has
created all of our menus since then, and our customers love his food.

We will be very sorry to see Julio leave, but he is ready to take on more
responsibilities. I am confident he would be a great addition to your team.
If you have any questions, please contact me at 714-444-3232.

Sincerely,
Randy Schumann
Manager, Geos Bar & Grill
Fullerton, CA

---

30. What is the main idea that Randy wants to communicate in the letter?

A. Julio would be excellent for the chef's job at the Beef House.

B. Randy has known Julio for five years.

C. Julio likes working at Geos Bar & Grill.

D. Julio has created good menus, and the customers love his food.

31. Who is Randy Schumann?

A. He is applying for a job.

B. He is one of Julio's coworkers.

C. He is a customer.

D. He is Julio's manager.

32. What does Randy not say about Julio?

A. He is creative.

B. He is dependable.

C. He is confident.

D. He is hardworking.

33. Read the article again. What inference can you make?

A. Julio has worked for Geos Bar & Grill for five years.

B. The Beef House is a smaller restaurant than Geos Bar & Grill.

C. Geos Bar & Grill is closing down.

D. Julio is leaving because he's tired of being a cook.

Unit 5 Test

🔘 LISTENING I

(Tracks 27-28) **You will hear a question. Then you will hear a conversation. After that, you will hear the question again and three choices. What is the correct answer: A, B, or C?**

1. A. The man can't get a luggage tag.
   B. The man can't check the bag with his luggage.
   C. The man can't take the bag with him onto the plane.

2. A. He needs to see the woman's boarding pass and round-trip ticket.
   B. He needs to see the woman's photo ID and boarding pass.
   C. He needs to see the woman's photo ID and carry-on bag.

🔘 LISTENING II

(Tracks 29-30) **You will hear the first part of a conversation. To finish the conversation, listen and choose the correct answer: A, B, or C.**

3. A. I took the wrong bus.
   B. It's 7:30.
   C. Sure. I'll be there in five minutes.

4. A. OK. I'll call you when I land.
   B. Just a medium-size suitcase and a small carry-on.
   C. I'll meet you at baggage claim.

🔘 LISTENING III

(Tracks 31-32) **You will hear a conversation. Then you will hear three sentences. Which sentence is true: A, B, or C?**

5. A. The man will stay in Chicago for the night.
   B. The man's flight was delayed.
   C. The man missed his flight.

6. A. The man thinks they should go to Gate 30.
   B. The woman thinks they should check the screen.
   C. The woman thinks they should go to Gate 13.

LIFE SKILLS

Read the screen instructions. Then answer the questions. What is the correct answer: A, B, C, or D?

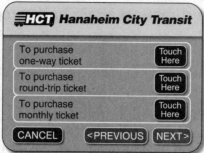

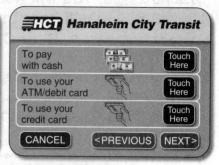

7. You want to buy a one-way ticket. You pressed Monthly Ticket by mistake and you are now on the payment screen. Which button should you press?

    A. CANCEL

    B. PREVIOUS

    C. NEXT

    D. To purchase one-way ticket

8. Which instruction tells you to put your ATM card in the machine?

    A. To use your ATM/debit card

    B. To use your credit card

    C. Touch Here

    D. Please insert your ATM/debit card now.

9. You bought a ticket. Now you want to buy another ticket. Which button should you press?

    A. CANCEL

    B. To purchase more tickets

    C. To print ticket(s)

    D. PREVIOUS

10. You thought you could buy a ticket, but you don't have enough money. Which button should you press?

    A. CANCEL

    B. To print ticket(s)

    C. PREVIOUS

    D. NEXT

GRAMMAR

Complete each conversation. What is the correct answer: A, B, or C?

11. **A:** You _____ take scissors on the plane. They're not allowed.
    B: OK. I'll pack them in my luggage.

    A. could
    B. can't
    C. couldn't

12. **A:** They said we have a new gate. We have to go to Gate 7.
    B: What did you say? It's so noisy, I _____ hear you.

    A. won't be able to
    B. can't
    C. couldn't

13. **A:** We _____ board now. They just called our section.
    B: Great. Let me get my bag.

    A. can
    B. can't
    C. couldn't

14. **A:** How was your flight?
    B: Well, my original flight got canceled. But I _____ able to get on another one two hours later.

    A. won't be
    B. wasn't
    C. was

15. **A:** Tomas _____ able to take his juice on the plane.
    B: OK. I'll tell him to drink it now.

    A. wasn't
    B. won't be
    C. will be

16. **A:** Is that my water bottle or _____?

    B: It's mine.

    A. you

    B. your

    C. yours

17. **A:** Did you forget your bag on the bus?

    B: No. _____ bag is right here.

    A. Mine

    B. My

    C. Yours

18. **A:** Is that our car over there?

    B: Yeah, that's _____.

    A. ours

    B. our

    C. yours

19. **A:** Is this her suitcase?

    B: No. _____ is already checked.

    A. Her

    B. Mine

    C. Hers

20. **A:** Is this our car or Pete and Mary's?

    B: It's not ours. It's _____.

    A. their

    B. theirs

    C. there's

21. **A:** Could I please have a bus schedule?
    B: Yes, of course you _____. Here you go!

    A. could
    B. can
    C. would

22. **A:** Could you _____ me a favor?
    B: Sure. What is it?

    A. do
    B. does
    C. doing

23. **A:** Would you please _____ my bag for me?
    B: Sure. No problem.

    A. watching
    B. watched
    C. watch

24. **A:** _____ I have a transfer ticket?
    B: OK. Here you are.

    A. Could
    B. Would
    C. Will

25. **A:** Excuse me. _____ you please sit down?
    B: Of course. I'm sorry.

    A. Can't
    B. Would
    C. May

VOCABULARY

Read. What is the correct answer: A, B, C, or D?

26. Please put your carry-on bags in the _____ above your seat.

    A. boarding pass

    B. bins

    C. arrivals and departures

    D. metal detector

27. You may take one _____ and one personal item on the plane.

    A. gate

    B. luggage

    C. carry-on bag

    D. luggage tags

28. If you need to change your seat, talk to the _____.

    A. metal detector

    B. ticket agent

    C. passenger

    D. kiosk

29. Your flight will leave from _____ 47.

    A. Kiosk

    B. Passenger

    C. Arrivals and departures

    D. Gate

READING

Read. What is the correct answer: A, B, C, or D?

Last summer I took my family to visit relatives in Mexico City, Mexico. We flew from Chicago to Mexico City. Unfortunately, we had several problems along the way. First, my wife forgot our passports when we left home. We had to drive back and get them. Then, when we got to the airport, we missed our flight and had to go on stand-by. We waited for hours. Finally, we got onto a flight in the afternoon and we landed in Mexico City around 10:00 P.M.

Then we went to the baggage claim area, but our bags never came. We talked to a customer service agent, and she said that our bags were accidentally sent to El Paso, Texas! Fortunately, our bags were already on the way to Mexico City, and the agent said they would be delivered to our hotel.

So we got into a taxi and headed to our hotel. When we arrived, I couldn't find my wallet. And then I remembered that it was in the pocket of my jacket—back home in Chicago! Luckily, my wife had her wallet, with money and her ID, so she checked us in to the hotel. The next morning our luggage arrived. What an adventure!

30. What is the main idea of the story?

A. The man lost his wallet, but he got it later.

B. The family missed their flight.

C. The family had many problems on their way to Mexico.

D. The man's wife forgot the passports at home.

31. Which of these problems happened first?

A. The family missed their flight.

B. The family had to go back home to get their passports.

C. The luggage was missing.

D. The man couldn't find his wallet.

32. Which did not happen?

A. The family went to El Paso, Texas.

B. The luggage went to El Paso, Texas.

C. The man's wallet was in his jacket.

D. The man's wife forgot the passports.

33. Read the story again. Based on the information in the story, what inference can you make?

A. The family always has problems.

B. The hotel was expensive.

C. The airport in Mexico City was hot.

D. The man didn't need his wallet during the trip.

Unit 6 Test

🔘 LISTENING I

(Tracks 33-34) **You will hear a question. Then you will hear a conversation. After that, you will hear the question again and three choices. What is the correct answer: A, B, or C?**

1. A. The vacuum cleaner bag doesn't fit.
   B. The power cord is frayed.
   C. The vacuum cleaner is expensive.

2. A. if the microwave is still under warranty
   B. if the microwave is working
   C. if he can fix the microwave himself

🔘 LISTENING II

(Tracks 35-36) **You will hear the first part of a conversation. To finish the conversation, listen and choose the correct answer: A, B, or C.**

3. A. I can't get good service around my house.
   B. OK. First, why was I charged a $15.00 activation fee?
   C. So what happened?

4. A. There's a problem with my bill.
   B. My current plan is $39.99 per month.
   C. No, I don't. But I know I need more minutes.

🔘 LISTENING III

(Tracks 37-38) **You will hear a conversation. Then you will hear three sentences. Which sentence is true: A, B, or C?**

5. A. The man thinks the remote control is broken.
   B. The man doesn't have a receipt.
   C. The man thinks he can fix the remote control.

6. A. The man wants to buy a more expensive DVD player.
   B. The man wants to buy a cheaper DVD player.
   C. The man will get cash back.

LIFE SKILLS

Read. What is the correct answer: A, B, C, or D?

7. How much is the manufacturer's rebate?
   A. $200.00
   B. $1199.99
   C. $1399.99
   D. $1899.99

8. What is the cost of the TV on sale after the rebate?
   A. $1999.99
   B. $1399.99
   C. $1199.99
   D. $200.00

9. For how long is the offer valid?
   A. 48 months
   B. 90 days
   C. as long as supplies last
   D. one week

10. How many televisions can you get a rebate on?
    A. one
    B. two
    C. as many as you want
    D. none

GRAMMAR

Complete each conversation. What is the correct answer: A, B, or C?

11. **A:** The TV won't turn on.
    B: Do you think _____?

    A. is it broken
    B. it's broken
    C. that is broken

12. **A:** The microwave cord is frayed.
    B: Do you think _____?

    A. you can fix it
    B. can you fix it
    C. that you can

13. **A:** I'm afraid _____.
    B: Well, I guess we'll have to call the service repair center.

    A. that can't fix it
    B. can't I fix it
    C. that I can't fix it

14. **A.** Do you have proof of purchase?
    B. I think _____, but I'll look.

    A. yes
    B. so
    C. I have

15. **A.** Is the product still under warranty?
    B. We bought it more than five years ago, so _____ so.

    A. I think not
    B. I don't think
    C. I think no

16. **A:** I like this TV because the picture is _____ than the other one.

   B: Yeah, I can see that too.

   A. brighter

   B. bright

   C. as bright

17. **A:** What do you think about your new cell phone plan?

   B: Well, I think I made a mistake. This plan is _____ than my last one.

   A. bad

   B. worse

   C. as bad

18. **A:** Is this DVD player _____ than the first one we looked at?

   B: I'm not sure. Let's check.

   A. expensive

   B. less expensive

   C. as expensive

19. **A:** This vacuum cleaner is _____ than that one.

   B: I know, but it's also more expensive!

   A. quiet

   B. as quiet

   C. quieter

20. **A:** The new TV has a really big screen, so we can sit _____ we did before.

   B: And more people can watch it!

   A. farther away than

   B. far away

   C. far away than

21. **A:** I like the first refrigerator we saw.
    B: I agree. This one is _____ as that one.

    A. not better
    B. not good
    C. not as good

22. **A:** What do you think about this DVD player?
    B: Hmm. Well, it isn't _____ as the other one.

    A. as expensive
    B. more expensive
    C. expensive

23. **A:** I like to shop at Thriftway. Their lines are not _____ Shop & Save.
    B: I agree. I don't like going to Shop & Save.

    A. as long
    B. as long as
    C. long as

24. **A:** I like to shop at Save Max because they have the best prices.
    B: Really? I think Quickee Stop's prices are just _____.

    A. cheap as
    B. as cheap as
    C. as cheap

25. **A:** Shopping online is just _____ as shopping in a store.
    B: Yeah, the Internet is safer now.

    A. as safe
    B. safe
    C. safer

VOCABULARY

Read. What is the correct answer: A, B, C, or D?

26.

The plug on this toaster is _____.

A. leaking

B. frayed

C. scratched

D. bent

27.

This CD is _____. I can't play it.

A. cracked

B. frayed

C. leaking

D. dented

28.

The car is _____. It was in an accident.

A. cracked

B. defective

C. dented

D. scratched

29.

There's a problem with the air conditioner. It's _____.

A. dented

B. leaking

C. scratched

D. bent

READING

Read. What is the correct answer: A, B, C, or D?

Antonio's Shopping Surprise

Antonio Mendoza lived in El Paso, Texas, with his wife Amanda and their three children: Everett, eleven years old, Lucille, seven years old, and Eduardo, five years old. It was getting close to the holidays. Christmas was only two weeks away, and Antonio wanted to make this Christmas the best ever. Antonio asked his family to write a list of the things they wanted for Christmas. When Antonio read everyone's list, he thought, "How can I pay for all these things?" Everett wants a computer. Lucille and Eduardo want a video game system. Amanda wants a new cell phone.

Antonio asked for extra hours at work. Even with the extra pay, he thought it would be difficult to make enough money to pay for all the gifts. For several days in a row, Antonio would go out shopping after work. He would visit all the stores in the area, looking for the best prices. However, he couldn't find any good deals. Everything was so expensive!

One day at work Antonio heard a couple of his coworkers talking. They were talking about Digital Discounters, a new electronics store in town that had just opened. Antonio heard the men talking about some great deals on all kinds of electronics. The next day, Antonio checked his mail and noticed that there was a sales flyer from the new store. Antonio saw great prices on computers, video game systems, and cell phones. He circled the things he wanted to buy. He took the flyer to the store, and a sales associate helped him find everything he needed. Antonio even had enough money left over to buy his wife a nice pair of earrings. Now Antonio was sure this would be the best Christmas ever!

---

30. What is the main idea of the story?

   A. Antonio worked extra hours to pay for his family's Christmas gifts.

   B. Antonio's children wanted a computer and a video game system.

   C. Antonio needed to find a way to buy the things his family wanted for Christmas, and he did.

   D. Antonio bought his Christmas gifts at Digital Discounters.

31. What is not described in the story?

   A. Antonio's children wanted a television.

   B. Antonio's wife wanted a cell phone.

   C. Antonio worked extra hours.

   D. Antonio went shopping after work.

32. How did Antonio solve his problem?

   A. He only bought some things his family wanted.

   B. He changed jobs.

   C. He went to a store that had great deals.

   D. He took his family on a vacation.

33. Read the story again. Based on the information in the story, what inference can you make?

   A. Amanda broke her cell phone.

   B. Everett is a good student.

   C. Eduardo is too young for a video game system.

   D. Antonio doesn't make a lot of money.

Unit 7 Test

🔘 LISTENING I

(Tracks 39–40) You will hear a question. Then you will hear a conversation. After that, you will hear the question again and three choices. What is the correct answer: A, B, or C?

1. A. change the oil
    B. check the brakes
    C. rotate the tires

2. A. The woman doesn't have a license.
    B. The woman was speeding.
    C. There was an accident.

🔘 LISTENING II

(Tracks 41–42) You will hear the first part of a conversation. To finish the conversation, listen and choose the correct answer: A, B, or C.

3. A. In the trunk.
    B. Under the hood.
    C. In the glove compartment.

4. A. I have jumper cables.
    B. The battery is dead.
    C. I need a spare tire.

🔘 LISTENING III

(Tracks 43–44) You will hear a conversation. Then you will hear three sentences. Which sentence is true: A, B, or C?

5. A. There was an accident.
    B. There's a 25-minute delay.
    C. There's a traffic jam.

6. A. The accident caused a lot of traffic.
    B. Rubbernecking caused an accident.
    C. The weather caused an accident.

LIFE SKILLS

Read. What is the correct answer: A, B, C, or D?

7. Turn on your _____, and then change lanes.

   A. turn signal

   B. accelerator

   C. steering wheel

   D. sideview mirror

8. The _____ shows how fast you're driving.

   A. ignition

   B. gas pedal

   C. speedometer

   D. license plate

9. My car wouldn't start, so I opened the hood and looked at the _____.

   A. headlights

   B. engine

   C. bumper

   D. horn

10. She turned on her _____ because it was raining.

    A. gas gauge

    B. windshield

    C. brakes

    D. wipers

GRAMMAR

Complete each conversation. What is the correct answer: A, B, or C?

11. **A:** One of the tires on my car is flat.
    B: Oh, no. Do you have _____ spare tire?

    A. a
    B. an
    C. the

12. **A:** Where is your car's horn?
    B: It's on _____ steering wheel.

    A. a
    B. the
    C. an

13. **A:** Does your car have _____ air conditioner?
    B: Yes, but I don't use it very often.

    A. an
    B. a
    C. the

14. **A:** My car is making _____ strange noise.
    B: Maybe you should take it to a repair shop.

    A. the
    B. an
    C. a

15. **A:** Drive until you get to the light at the intersection of Jefferson Street and Third Avenue.
    B: OK. What do I do at _____ intersection?

    A. an
    B. the
    C. a

16. **A:** Did Lydia get hurt in the car accident?
    B: No. Luckily she _____ her seatbelt.

    A. were wearing
    B. wearing
    C. was wearing

17. **A:** How did the accident happen?
    B: I was _____, and I hit a parked car.

    A. backing up
    B. back up
    C. backed up

18. **A:** Why was there so much traffic?

    B: There was an accident, and drivers _____ down to see what happened.

    A. were slowing

    B. was slowing

    C. were slow

19. **A:** The car in front of me stopped suddenly, and I almost hit it.

    B: Well, luckily, you _____.

    A. not speeding

    B. weren't speeding

    C. didn't speed

20. **A:** It's so dangerous to drive and talk on a cell phone!

    B: I know. This morning a woman _____ on her phone, and she almost hit me.

    A. talking

    B. talked

    C. was talking

21. **A:** What should I do if I have a car accident?

    B: _____ first make sure everyone is OK.

    A. After you have an accident,

    B. After, you have an accident

    C. After you have it, an accident

22. **A:** You get better _____ your tires have the correct pressure.

    B: Really? I should check my tires.

    A. gas mileage, when

    B. gas mileage when

    C. gas mileage,

23. **A:** I'm taking cold medicine because I have a bad cold.

    B: Check _____ you drive. Some medications can make you sleepy.

    A. the bottle's label before

    B. the bottle's label before,

    C. the bottle's label, before

24. **A:** Be careful. Roads _____ after it rains.

    B: I know. Thanks.

    A. can be, slippery

    B. can be slippery,

    C. can be slippery

25. **A:** _____ I listen to the traffic report.

    B: That's a good idea.

    A. I leave the house

    B. Before I leave the house,

    C. Before I leave, the house

VOCABULARY

Read. What is the correct answer: A, B, C, or D?

26. After the accident, Mimi couldn't drive her car. A _____ had to move it.

A. construction

B. overpass

C. license

D. tow truck

27. Use the entrance ramp to _____ the highway.

A. park your car on

B. get off of

C. get onto

D. pass other cars on

28. At the _____ you have to pay for using the road.

A. toll booth

B. vehicle

C. overpass

D. lane

29. After the accident, the driver moved his car to the _____. Then it wasn't blocking traffic.

A. traffic jam

B. freeway

C. shoulder

D. vehicle

READING

Read. What is the correct answer: A, B, C, or D?

Hakan Damir didn't like to wear his seat belt. He had many reasons. He said, "It's uncomfortable," "I'm not driving far," and even "I'm a good driver." His wife Ela explained that it was illegal in their state to drive without a seatbelt. She said he should wear his seatbelt, but Hakan didn't agree.

Then, one day Ela was driving to the supermarket. It was less than one mile from their house. Ela was driving carefully and slowly. Suddenly another car came out of nowhere and hit Ela's car. Her car rolled over and over. The car was destroyed. But luckily, and most importantly, Ela walked away from the accident with just a few small injuries. A police officer at the accident said that the seatbelt saved her life.

That event taught Hakan a lesson. He still believes he's a good driver, and sometimes he thinks the seat belt is a little uncomfortable. But now he always wears it, even if he's driving a short distance.

Hakan isn't alone. More and more people are realizing the importance of seat belts. For example, many states require that adults use seat belts when they are in a moving car, and even more states now require children to wear seat belts. These new laws are saving lives and making people more conscious of driver safety.

---

30. What is the main idea of the story?

A. Hakan changed his opinion on wearing a seat belt.

B. More children are being saved from car accidents.

C. Ela had a serious car accident because she wasn't wearing her seat belt.

D. Hakan is uncomfortable driving with a seat belt.

31. What was Hakan's attitude toward seat belts?

A. He thought they were uncomfortable.

B. He thought they were not necessary.

C. He thought they were only important for long distances.

D. all of the above

Safety belt use laws in sample states, 2009

State	Must be in child restraint	Adult safety belt permissible	Maximum first offense
Arizona	4 years and younger	no	$50
Arkansas	5 years and younger or less than 60 pounds	6 through 15 years or 60+ pounds	$100
California	5 years and younger or less than 60 pounds	6 through 15 years or 60+ pounds	$100
Florida	3 years and younger	4 through 5 years	$60
Minnesota	3 years and younger	no	$50
Nevada	5 years and younger and 60 pounds or less	no	$500
Texas	4 years and younger and less than 36 inches	no	$200
Virginia	7 years and younger unless they have a physician exemption	8 through 15 years	$50

Source: www.iihs.org/laws/childrestraint.aspx

32. In which states do you pay the most money if you do not follow the law?

A. California and Texas

B. Nevada and Texas

C. Arkansas and California

D. Arkansas and Texas

33. What can be inferred from the chart?

A. Safety belts are not necessary for adults.

B. Most states do not require children to wear restraints.

C. Fines for safety belts are not expensive.

D. States have different laws and fines regarding safety belts for children.

Unit 8 Test

💿 LISTENING I

(Tracks 45–46) **You will hear a question. Then you will hear a conversation. After that, you will hear the question again and three choices. What is the correct answer: A, B, or C?**

1. A. salty foods like chips
   B. vegetables with dip
   C. carrots and celery

2. A. because she's late to work
   B. because she isn't hungry
   C. because she's busy with her children

💿 LISTENING II

(Tracks 47–48) **You will hear the first part of a conversation. To finish the conversation, listen and choose the correct answer: A, B, or C.**

3. A. I'd like a glass of milk with the cake.
   B. My son is allergic to dairy.
   C. Because it's a nut-free cake.

4. A. You should do it every day.
   B. It's not a good idea to do.
   C. After I brush my teeth.

💿 LISTENING III

(Tracks 49–50) **You will hear a conversation. Then you will hear three sentences. Which sentence is true: A, B, or C?**

5. A. Chicken is low in protein.
   B. Fish is high in protein.
   C. Turkey is high in fat.

6. A. Babies under twelve months old can drink whole milk.
   B. Children who are one to two years old can drink whole milk.
   C. Children who are over two years old cannot drink low-fat milk.

LIFE SKILLS

Read. What is the correct answer: A, B, C, or D?

Plain Non-fat Yogurt

Nutrition Facts
Serving Size 1 container (226g)

Amount Per Serving

Calories 110	Calories from Fat 0

	% Daily Value
Total Fat 0g	**0%**
Saturated Fat 0g	**7%**
Trans Fat 0g	**0%**
Cholesterol Less than 5mg	
Sodium 160mg	**7%**
Total Carbohydrate 15g	**5%**
Dietary Fiber 0g	**0%**
Sugars 0g	
Protein 10g	

Vitamin A 0%	**Vitamin C** 4%
Calcium 45%	**Iron** 0%

*Percent Daily Values are based on a 2,000 calorie diet. Your Daily Values may be higher or lower depending on your calorie needs.

Strawberry Cream Yogurt

Nutrition Facts
Serving Size 1 container (227g)

Amount Per Serving

Calories 240	Calories from Fat 25

	% Daily Value
Total Fat 3g	**4%**
Saturated Fat 1.5g	**9%**
Trans Fat 0g	**0%**
Cholesterol 15mg	**5%**
Sodium 140mg	**6%**
Total Carbohydrate 46g	**15%**
Dietary Fiber Less than 1g	**3%**
Sugars 44g	
Protein 9g	

Vitamin A 2%	**Vitamin C** 4%
Calcium 35%	**Iron** 0%

*Percent Daily Values are based on a 2,000 calorie diet. Your Daily Values may be higher or lower depending on your calorie needs.

7. The strawberry cream yogurt has _____ calories from fat.

   A. 3

   B. 25

   C. 110

   D. 240

8. The plain and strawberry cream yogurt have the same amount of _____.

   A. calories

   B. cholesterol

   C. *trans* fats

   D. protein

9. The strawberry cream yogurt has a lot more _____ than the plain yogurt.

   A. vitamins

   B. sodium

   C. dietary fiber

   D. sugars

10. The plain yogurt has _____ of the daily value for carbohydrates.

    A. 5 percent

    B. 15 grams

    C. 15 percent

    D. 46 grams

GRAMMAR

Complete each conversation. What is the correct answer: A, B, or C?

11. **A:** Do you ever stay up late on weeknights?
    B: No, I _____ go to bed by 11 P.M.

    A. never
    B. always
    C. rarely

12. **A:** Do you take vitamins?
    B: Yes, I _____ take a vitamin with breakfast, but if I forget, I take it before I go to bed.

    A. never
    B. always
    C. usually

13. **A:** How often do you get a physical examination?
    B: I've _____ gotten one.

    A. never
    B. always
    C. usually

14. **A:** Do your kids eat vegetables every day?
    B: Well, I give them vegetables every day, but they don't _____ eat them.

    A. never
    B. sometimes
    C. always

15. **A:** I _____ use canola oil when I cook because it's better for you than peanut oil.
    B: Hmm. I should try that.

    A. often
    B. rarely
    C. never

16. **A:** My doctor says I need to exercise, but I don't like _____.
    B: If you take fast walks, that's also good for you.

    A. running
    B. run
    C. runs

17. **A:** Raul, you should really stop _____.
    B: I know. I'm trying to quit.

    A. smoke
    B. smoking
    C. to smoke

18. **A:** I'm on a diet, but it's so hard to lose weight.
    B: Don't give up. Keep _____.

    A. to try
    B. try
    C. trying

19. **A:** I need to exercise, but I can't go outdoors in the winter.
    B: Try _____ up and down the stairs inside your apartment building.

    A. walk
    B. walking
    C. walks

20. **A:** I'm sorry, I only have low-fat milk.
    B: That's all right. I don't mind _____ low-fat.

    A. drinking
    B. to drink
    C. drink

21. **A:** _____ your hands before you eat will help you avoid getting a cold.
    B: Right. I'll go wash them now.

    A. Wash
    B. Washing
    C. To wash

22. **A:** _____ small, healthy snacks during the day is better for you than eating big meals.
    B: That may be true, but I still like big, hot meals.

    A. Eating
    B. To eat
    C. Eat

23. **A:** Why did the dentist say to use a soft toothbrush?
    B: Because _____ with a soft toothbrush is gentler on your teeth.

    A. brush
    B. brushes
    C. brushing

24. **A:** _____ a lot of water is good for you, but why?
    B: Lots of reasons. It makes your skin healthier and gives you more energy.

    A. Drinking
    B. Drinks of
    C. Drink

25. **A:** When I need to diet, I just skip meals.
    B: But _____ meals is bad for your body, and it's not an effective way to lose weight.

    A. skip
    B. skipping
    C. skipped

VOCABULARY

Read. What is the correct answer: A, B, C, or D?

26. I try not to _____, but the candy bars in the vending machines always look so good.

    A. eat fast food

    B. be on a diet

    C. drink sugary beverages

    D. buy junk food

27. If you don't want to _____, try using low-fat ingredients in your cooking.

    A. eat home-cooked meals

    B. get take out

    C. eat fatty foods

    D. eat fast food

28. There are a lot of McDonald's and Burger Kings in my neighborhood, but I try not to _____.

    A. eat fast food

    B. have snacks

    C. buy frozen dinners

    D. drink sugary beverages

29. I like to go to the A & C supermarket to _____ because their prices are good.

    A. eat fast food

    B. buy fresh fruits and vegetables

    C. have a snack

    D. eat fatty foods

READING

Read. What is the correct answer: A, B, C, or D?

Los Angeles is going green! In Los Angeles County, the University of California has a program called Common Ground to sustain community gardens in L.A. and teach people to grow their own food. Hilda Suarez is one member of the program. Hilda was looking for ways to save money on her monthly budget. She realized that if she grew her own fruits and vegetables, she could save over $50 a month. But since Hilda lived in an apartment building, she thought she could never have her own garden. Then a friend, Juanita, told her about Common Ground. Now Hilda grows squash, lettuce, and tomatoes at the Francis Avenue garden, one of the many gardens in L.A. She also grows some vegetables from Mexico, such as jicama, a flavorful root. When Hilda first joined the program, she didn't know much about gardening. But at the Common Ground program, some experienced gardeners gave free workshops and she learned gardening techniques. They also gave her some free seeds. Now Hilda likes to bring family members to her little patch. Thanks to Common Ground, Hilda is not only saving money; she also has a fun activity for her family to do together on weekends.

30. What is the main idea of the article?

A. Hilda Suarez is saving money by gardening.

B. Los Angeles has community gardens.

C. Common Ground is a program that helps people to build community gardens.

D. Community gardens are a way to make the planet green.

31. Why did Hilda Suarez join Common Ground?

A. To make extra money as a part-time job

B. To learn farming techniques

C. To spend time with her family

D. To save money on fruits and vegetables

32. What is Hilda growing in her garden, according to the article?

A. potatoes, peas, and carrots

B. lettuce, tomatoes, jicama, and squash

C. squash, potatoes, lettuce, and tomatoes

D. jicama, flowers, tomatoes, and cucumbers

33. Which sentence below gives an opinion in the article?

A. Gardening is a fun activity for Hilda to do with her family.

B. Hilda didn't know much about gardening when she started.

C. Hilda realized if she grew her own fruits and vegetables, she could save over $50 a month.

D. Hilda likes to bring family members to her garden patch.

Unit 9 Test

🖸 LISTENING I

(Tracks 51–52) You will hear a question. Then you will hear a conversation. After that, you will hear the question again and three choices. What is the correct answer: A, B, or C?

1. A. He wants time off to go to Florida.
   B. He wants Ms. Li to meet his cousin.
   C. He wants to take next Friday off.

2. A. He wants Ana not to interrupt him during his meeting.
   B. He wants Ana to go to a meeting.
   C. He wants Ana to call some people back for him.

🖸 LISTENING II

(Tracks 53–54) You will hear the first part of a conversation. To finish the conversation, listen and choose the correct answer: A, B, or C.

3. A. Continue driving and watching the road carefully.
   B. Stop the bus and speak to the child who is causing trouble.
   C. Report any mechanical problems to the bus company.

4. A. The ones on the top shelf in the right corner.
   B. You need to take inventory of the medications.
   C. Could you please ring up this customer?

🖸 LISTENING III

(Tracks 55–56) You will hear a conversation. Then you will hear three sentences. Which sentence is true: A, B, or C?

5. A. The shipment will arrive on January 5th.
   B. The shipment will arrive on January 6th.
   C. The shipment will be a week late.

6. A. Hakkim yelled at his coworker, Adina.
   B. Hakkim yelled at his employer, Marjorie.
   C. Hakkim was working slowly.

LIFE SKILLS

Read. What is the correct answer: A, B, C, or D?

Blackman Company Safety Rules

Attention employees: Be aware of safety hazards. Follow the safety procedures.

Prevent Slips, Trips, and Falls.
- Always clean up the work area.
- Make sure wires and equipment are kept out of the way.
- Use caution when walking on wet or slippery floors.
- Wear non-slip shoes.

Operate Machinery Carefully.
- Turn off machinery before cleaning or repairing.
- Turn off machinery when not in use.
- Wear eye protection (goggles) or a face shield.
- Keep hands at a safe distance from machinery.
- Do not wear loose fitting clothes or long sleeves when operating machines.

7. Walking on wet floors can be dangerous because _____.
   A. you might slip and fall
   B. you might trip over wires
   C. you need to use caution
   D. water is a safety hazard

8. You should operate machinery _____.
   A. when not in use
   B. during repairs
   C. while cleaning it
   D. with appropriate protection

9. It is the responsibility of employees _____.
   A. to know safety rules
   B. to follow safety procedures
   C. to be aware of safety hazards
   D. all of the above

10. When you have finished work, _____.
   A. wear non-slip shoes
   B. clean up the work area
   C. wear loose-fitting clothes
   D. leave machinery on

GRAMMAR

Complete each conversation. What is the correct answer: A, B, or C?

11. **A:** Which box do you need me to get?

    B: I need _____ over there. With the shipping labels.

    A. which one

    B. that one

    C. this one

12. **A:** Which takeout order is yours?

    B: _____ that says "Delfino" on it.

    A. The one

    B. Which one

    C. The ones

13. **A:** Your truck needs a tune-up? _____ is yours?

    B: The one over there. The 1990 Great Dane SS Reefer.

    A. Which one

    B. This one

    C. The one

14. **A:** Some of the cleaning products have dangerous chemicals in them.
    You should be careful when you use those products.

    B: _____ are dangerous?

    A. That one

    B. Which ones

    C. This one

15. **A:** You need to be careful with these chemicals. This one can burn your hands.
    And _____ can blind your eyes.

    B: Are there different products I can use instead?

    A. that one

    B. which one

    C. the ones

16. **A:** My employer expects us _____ a time card.
    B: Oh. At my job, we just sign in.

    A. to punch
    B. punch
    C. punching

17. **A:** Do you need us _____ overtime tonight?
    B: No, I think we should be able to finish on time.

    A. work
    B. to work
    C. not working

18. **A:** Does the manager really _____ clean up our stations and close everything down by 10 P.M.?
    B: Yes, he does.

    A. expect us to
    B. expects us to
    C. expect them to

19. **A:** Didn't the floor supervisor warn you _____ before you clean it?
    B: Yes, he did. I guess I wasn't listening.

    A. to turn off the machine
    B. he turned off the machine
    C. turning off the machine

20. **A:** I would really like you _____ next weekend. Could you?
    B: Sure, no problem.

    A. to work
    B. work
    C. works

21. **A:** The manager told _____ a special on that car.
    B: OK. What discount are we taking off?

    A. to give
    B. we give
    C. us to give

22. **A:** Mr. Venutti told _____.
    B: Yes, there's going to be a category 3 hurricane.

    A. us to close the store early
    B. to close the store early
    C. us close the store early

23. **A:** The manager asked us _____ before returning to work.
    B: Well, of course. I know that.

    A. washes our hands
    B. washing our hands
    C. to wash our hands

24. **A:** The supervisor told _____ long sleeves when operating this machine.
    B: OK, I'll change clothes.

    A. not to wear
    B. not wear
    C. us not to wear

25. **A:** Didn't you _____ to draw on the school bus seats?
    B: I did, but those kids never listen to me.

    A. to tell them not
    B. tell them not
    C. tell them no

VOCABULARY

Read. What is the correct answer: A, B, C, or D?

26. Today the company wants us to _____. They are going to teach us how to use Microsoft Excel.

    A. train other employees

    B. follow instructions

    C. attend a training session

    D. give instructions

27. It is important for the manager to be able to _____ with employees.

    A. attend a training session

    B. discuss a problem

    C. give instructions

    D. give someone feedback

28. As the assistant manager, one of your most important job responsibilities will be to _____.

    A. train other employees

    B. discuss a problem

    C. be part of a team

    D. give someone feedback

29. When your manager tells you to do something, it is important to _____.

    A. give instructions

    B. deal with complaints

    C. be part of a team

    D. follow instructions

READING

Read. What is the correct answer: A, B, C, or D?

Erika Montes created a successful career for herself in the United States after only being here for a short time. After finishing high school in Juarez, Mexico, Montes went to Oregon to live with her father. When she first arrived, she knew only a little English. Her first job was at the Astoria Golf and Country Club. Then she decided to apply for a job as a teller at U.S. Bank. It was a scary decision because Montes didn't speak perfect English. But she was hired and quickly moved up in the bank. She started out as a teller, then became a universal banker, and was then promoted to teller coordinator. She now coordinates the work of four bank tellers. Montes is now fluent in Spanish and English, so she is one of the only tellers who can communicate with the growing number of Hispanic customers that the bank serves. Montes's colleagues and supervisors think highly of her. They think she enhances the bank by broadening its customer base. They appreciate her friendliness and work ethic. As for Montes, she sees her work at the bank as a career, and she may eventually go to college. Montes says that her strong work ethic is the result of her mother, who always pushed her to be the best she could be.

30. What is the main idea of the article?

A. Erika Montes is a bank employee who is fluent in Spanish and English.

B. Erika Montes received many promotions in a short time at a bank.

C. Erika Montes got her strong work ethic from her mother.

D. Erika Montes successfully started a career in the United States after moving from Juarez, Mexico.

31. What do Erika's employers think of her work?

A. They think she is a great employee.

B. They think she needs to work harder to be promoted from teller.

C. They think she needs to communicate more with customers.

D. They have noted some mistakes she has made in English.

32. What is a reason Erika was promoted at the bank?

A. She helped increase its number of customers.

B. She told the customers how to file tax returns.

C. She has connections with her colleagues and supervisors.

D. She is friendly.

33. What did Erika get from her mother?

A. a desire to work longer hours

B. a desire to be the best she can be

C. a desire to become a bank president

D. a desire to broaden her customer base

Unit 10 Test

🔘 LISTENING I

(Tracks 57–58) **You will hear a question. Then you will hear a conversation. After that, you will hear the question again and three choices. What is the correct answer: A, B, or C?**

1. A. He is making an appointment.
    B. He is canceling an appointment.
    C. He is asking to work on a different day.

2. A. She has back pain and headaches.
    B. She has headaches and nausea.
    C. She has stomach pain and nausea.

🔘 LISTENING II

(Tracks 59–60) **You will hear the first part of a conversation. To finish the conversation, listen and choose the correct answer: A, B, or C.**

3. A. No, I don't think I ever had them before.
    B. I think I'm all better now.
    C. Can you tell me what causes migraines?

4. A. I think the medication you gave me is helping.
    B. I'm having trouble sleeping.
    C. But what is causing the heartburn?

🔘 LISTENING III

(Tracks 61–62) **You will hear a conversation. Then you will hear three sentences. Which sentence is true: A, B, or C?**

5. A. Yuan Deng needs to change his doctor appointment.
    B. The doctor is not available on Thursday or Friday.
    C. Dr. Hops does not work at the clinic on Thursdays.

6. A. The patient sleeps too many hours.
    B. The patient is often thirsty during the night.
    C. The doctor is going to test the patient's blood.

LIFE SKILLS

Read. What is the correct answer: A, B, C, or D?

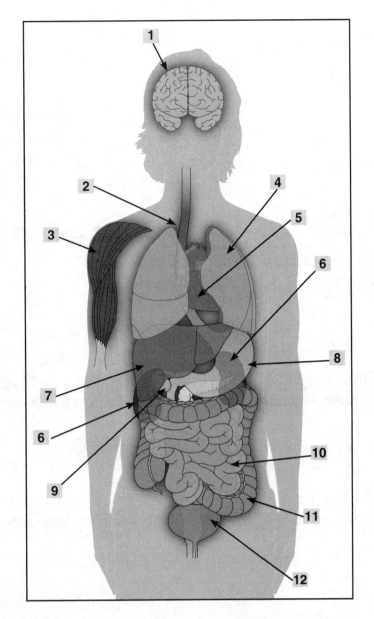

7. Which part of the body is number 4?

  A. the esophagus

  B. the liver

  C. the lungs

  D. the heart

8. Which part of the body is number 5?

  A. the esophagus

  B. the heart

  C. the liver

  D. the stomach

9. Which part of the body is number 6?

  A. the kidneys

  B. the stomach

  C. the small intestine

  D. the large intestine

10. Which part of the body is number 11?

  A. the liver

  B. the kidneys

  C. the small intestine

  D. the large intestine

GRAMMAR

Complete each conversation. What is the correct answer: A, B, or C?

11. **A:** What's the matter?

    B: The directions on this bottle are _____.

    A. confused

    B. confuses

    C. confusing

12. **A:** Doctor, I'm _____ about having glaucoma.

    B: Don't worry, Mr. Nguyen. We caught the problem early enough.

    A. worried

    B. worries

    C. worry

13. **A:** So Mrs. Escobar, what brings you here today?

    B: Well, I've been very _____, and I have nausea.

    A. tiring

    B. tired

    C. tiresome

14. **A:** I've been waiting in the ER for six hours already. It's very _____!

    B: Tell the receptionist how long you've been here. Maybe then they'll call your name soon.

    A. frustrated

    B. frustrates

    C. frustrating

15. **A:** I'm sorry to hear your uncle is in the hospital, Mi-Young.

    B: Thanks. He's a little _____, but our family stays with him all the time to cheer him up.

    A. depressed

    B. depressing

    C. depress

16. **A:** Mr. Santiago, have you been _____ as I suggested?
    B: Yes, doctor. I try to take a walk every day.

    A. exercising
    B. exercise
    C. exercised

17. **A:** Mrs. Chen, can you tell me why you haven't been taking your medication?
    B: Well, doctor, I've _____ trouble swallowing the pills.

    A. be having
    B. am having
    C. been having

18. **A:** Doctor Ortiz, what can I do? I can't sleep at night. _____ taking over-the-counter medications for two weeks to go to sleep.
    B: You should never take those medications for that long.

    A. I've been
    B. I am
    C. I haven't been

19. **A:** Doctor, I think I'm allergic to the medication you prescribed. I _____ a red rash.
    B: Stop taking it immediately. I'll prescribe something else.

    A. has been getting
    B. will be getting
    C. have been getting

20. **A:** Ms. Park, I'm missing some information on your medical history form. _____ any medications?
    B: Just lisinopril for high blood pressure.

    A. Do you plan to take
    B. Have you been taking
    C. You've taken

21. **A:** Mrs. Caruso, could you tell me why you haven't been taking your medicine?
    B: Well, doctor, I don't really believe _____ taking medicine.

    A. about
    B. at
    C. in

22. **A:** Congratulations, Mrs. Du Bois. Your operation was a success.
    B: Thank you, doctor. I can't wait to leave the hospital. And I'm looking forward _____ eating food again!

    A. about
    B. in
    C. to

23. **A:** What seems to be the problem with your mother, Mrs. Zapata?
    B: She's complaining _____ forgetting things lately.

    A. about
    B. at
    C. in

24. **A:** Doctor, I'm worried _____ getting the operation. I think the insurance might not pay for the medications I'll need after the operation.
    B: Don't worry, Ms. Hussein. We'll call the insurance company and find out.

    A. of
    B. about
    C. to

25. **A:** Desirée, I'm not sure I can take you to your doctor's appointment. Will it be a problem?
    B: It will be OK. If you can't take me, I'll plan _____ taking the bus.

    A. to
    B. of
    C. on

VOCABULARY

Read. What is the correct answer: A, B, C, or D?

26. Jung went to the _____ to do some blood work.

    A. surgery

    B. radiology

    C. physical therapy

    D. laboratory

27. Chanté just had her baby. I'm going to go see her at _____.

    A. pediatrics

    B. admissions

    C. the maternity ward

    D. surgery

28. If you need help getting out of bed, press this button and someone from the _____ will come.

    A. nurse's station

    B. physical therapy

    C. intensive care unit

    D. emergency room

29. Gall bladder operations do not take very long. Patients are usually in _____ for about an hour and rest for a few hours after that.

    A. the emergency room

    B. surgery

    C. the intensive care unit

    D. radiology

READING

Read. What is the correct answer: A, B, C, or D?

It can be frightening for a child to see the doctor. You can prepare your child and make the visit a better experience.

Prepare before you go. First, explain why you are going to the doctor. Help your child understand that the doctor is going to help him, not hurt him. If possible, take your child to other family members' doctor's appointments. This will help your child get used to the doctor's office. Also, bring a blanket, favorite toy, or favorite book to help calm your child during the visit.

Be ready during the visit. Bring a list of questions you have for the doctor. Make sure that you understand everything the doctor is saying. You can take notes and ask questions during the visit or call the doctor later. Let your child speak to the doctor if possible. Your child might tell the doctor something he or she didn't tell you. If your child misbehaves at the doctor's office, be patient. Your child may be frightened. Do not punish your child since this can make him or her more afraid of the doctor.

Talk to your child after the visit. Make sure your child accepts the doctor's orders, if the doctor gave any instructions. Also, speak to your child about the doctor. Let your child express his or her feelings.

30. What is the main idea of the article?

    A. You need to be sensitive to children's feelings.

    B. Children are afraid of doctors.

    C. You can make your child's visit to the doctor a better experience.

    D. You need to let your child tell his or her feelings during the visit.

31. What are you responsible for during and after the doctor visit?

    A. understanding what the doctor is saying

    B. letting your child ask the doctor questions

    C. making sure your child will do what the doctor says

    D. all of the above

32. What are the main points shown in the headings within this text?

    A. things you can tell your child to calm him or her during a doctor visit

    B. a list of questions to write before the visit

    C. steps you can take before, during, and after the doctors visit to prepare

    D. a list of instructions to follow after the visit

33. Why is it important for children to tell their feelings?

    A. It will take away their pain.

    B. It will make them feel less afraid.

    C. It will make them happier.

    D. It will make them less depressed.

Unit 11 Test

💿 **LISTENING I**

(Tracks 63–64) You will hear a question. Then you will hear a conversation. After that, you will hear the question again and three choices. What is the correct answer: A, B, or C?

1. A. water and gas
   B. all utilities
   C. a gas stove

2. A. Open a bank account and bank online.
   B. Sign up with your employer.
   C. Open a bank account and use direct deposit.

💿 **LISTENING II**

(Tracks 65–66) You will hear the first part of a conversation. To finish the conversation, listen and choose the correct answer: A, B, or C.

3. A. Why aren't you open on weekends?
   B. That's fine. I only use the ATM.
   C. All right, thanks. I need to find a bank that is open later.

4. A. Is parking available?
   B. Well, that might work.
   C. How much do the utilities cost?

💿 **LISTENING III**

(Tracks 67–68) You will hear a conversation. Then you will hear three sentences. Which sentence is true: A, B, or C?

5. A. The clerk needs to see a picture ID.
   B. The clerk does not need to see a utility bill.
   C. The customer does not have a social security card.

6. A. The man and woman already have a budget.
   B. The woman wants to save money for a car.
   C. The man and woman cannot pay their bills.

LIFE SKILLS

**Read the utility bill on the next page. Then answer the questions.
What is the correct answer: A, B, or C?**

7. The total amount now due is _____.
   A. $179.83
   B. $349.84
   C. $165.01

8. The taxes and fees due this month are _____.
   A. $4.75
   B. $5.00
   C. $5.03

9. Last month, the customer _____.
   A. used more gas and electricity
   B. moved to a new address
   C. did not pay the bill

10. You can save money on your utility bill by _____.
    A. turning up the heat
    B. turning down your thermostat
    C. buying a new thermostat

Your Account Number
500 862 659 1

Felicia Gomez
1485 Nelson Avenue
Bronx, New York 10452

More Phone Numbers
24-hour service and info
(800) 288-1000

Consolidated Energy
700 Westchester Avenue
White Plains, NY 10606
www.consolenergyny.com

Next meter reading date on or about December 12, 2010

Billing Period	**Meter Number**
From 10/09/10 to 11/09/10	02304455

Previous Charges	**Account Balance**
Total amount due at last billing	165.01
Payment OVERDUE—DUE 9/9/10 LATE PAYMENT FEE	5.00
Previous balance	170.01

Current Charges	**Amount**
Customer charge 30 Days	5.03
Gas and Electricity Charges	170.05
Taxes and Fees	4.75
Total gas charges (Including taxes and fees)	179.83
Total Amount Now Due	**349.84**

Current Amount Past Due if not paid by Dec 9, 2010.
A late charge of $5.00 may apply.

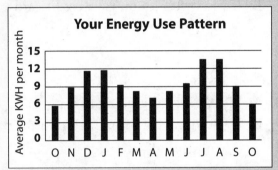

Your Energy Use Pattern

ENERGY SAVING TIP To save on your heating bill, set the thermostat lower. If you lower the thermostat slowly, over a few weeks, you will get used to the lower temperature.

Special DiscountYou may be eligible for California Alternate Rates for Energy (CARE) program. For more information and to request an application, please call 1-800-772-5050.

GRAMMAR

Complete each conversation. What is the correct answer: A, B, or C?

11. **A:** Where should we open our bank account?
    B: If we _____ at Central Bank, we get free checking.

    A. will bank
    B. banks
    C. bank

12. **A:** Why do I need to use a transaction register?
    B: If you _____ one, you can keep better track of your balance.

    A. use
    B. using
    C. will use

13. **A:** What are some reasons you can have bad credit?
    B: If you owe a lot on your credit cards, your credit score _____ down.

    A. go
    B. goes
    C. going

14. **A:** My ATM card is going to expire, and I didn't receive a new one yet.
    B: If you don't get the new card in the mail soon, _____ the bank.

    A. you will call
    B. you should call
    C. you don't call

15. **A:** I think someone stole my wallet.
    B: Well, if you _____ it soon, you need to cancel your credit cards.

    A. not find
    B. will not find
    C. don't find

16. **A:** My bills are so expensive. How can I save money on groceries?
    B: If you compare prices and buy specials, you _____ less for certain things.

    A. paid
    B. will pay
    C. pays

17. **A:** If I can't find someone to carpool with, I _____ be able to get to my new job.
    B: I'll ask my husband if he knows someone who can drive you.

    A. will
    B. am not
    C. won't

18. **A:** When I shop at the pharmacy, my bill is always so big.
    B: If you _____ store brand drugs, you'll save a lot.

    A. buy
    B. will buy
    C. have bought

19. **A:** I want to go shopping, but I can't find the coupons I saved.
    B: If you keep your coupons in the same place, you _____ to find them next time.

    A. will
    B. will be able
    C. are able

20. **A:** We're out of milk again. Can you buy some at the corner market?
    B: I don't want to go there. If I _____ it there, it will probably be old and go bad fast.

    A. get
    B. gets
    C. will get

21. **A:** Do you mind _____ so close to the subway?
    B: No, the noise doesn't bother me.

    A. live
    B. to live
    C. living

22. **A:** Do you need _____ downtown?
    B: No, I can live in the suburbs because I have a car.

    A. living
    B. to live
    C. live

23. **A:** I don't plan _____ until the middle of the month.
    B: OK, but I'm sorry, I still need the rent for all of October.

    A. to move in
    B. move in
    C. moving in

24. **A:** I want _____ an apartment with laundry in the basement.
    B: Well, we don't have a laundry room, but the laundromat is right across the street.

    A. find
    B. finding
    C. to find

25. **A:** Do you feel like _____ for apartments today?
    B: No, I don't. I'm really tired.

    A. to look
    B. looking
    C. look

VOCABULARY

Read. What is the correct answer: A, B, C, or D?

26. Sasha had to wait a long time in line to see the _____.

    A. ATM/debit card

    B. transaction register

    C. bank teller

    D. bank statement

27. Sorry, you can't make _____ here. The machine is broken.

    A. a bank statement

    B. an ATM withdrawal

    C. an ATM/debit card

    D. a transaction register

28. How much debt do you owe on your _____?

    A. bank statement

    B. balance

    C. check

    D. credit card

29. When you do an ATM withdrawal, you can find out your _____.

    A. balance

    B. ATM/debit card

    C. transaction register

    D. deposit slip

READING

Read. What is the correct answer: A, B, C, or D?

Marina Lopez is having money problems. Recently, she had a car accident, and her car was badly damaged. The repairs cost about $6500. Marina's insurance company will pay for most of the repairs, but Marina has to pay $500. Also, because Marina had an accident, her car insurance is going to go up from $200 a month to $240. The accident wasn't Marina's fault, but her insurance costs will go up anyway.

In addition to her money problems, Marina also needs to figure out how to get to work. The repairs to her car won't be finished for two weeks. Marina doesn't know anyone she can carpool with. She could take the bus, but it will take her two and a half hours to get to work. She can't rent a car because it would cost too much money. Marina can ask her parents to lend her their car, but then they will have to take the bus to work.

---

30. What is the main idea of the story?

A. Marina is doing a lot of repairs on her car.

B. Marina had a bad car accident.

C. Marina needs to travel a long way for her job.

D. Marina is having money problems and transportation problems.

31. How much do the repairs to Marina's car cost?

A. $200

B. $300

C. $500

D. $6500

32. Why is Marina's car insurance going up?

A. because she made late payments

B. because another family member drove her car

C. because she had a car accident

D. because the repairs are too expensive

33. What is the author's purpose?

A. to entertain

B. to talk about one person's problems

C. to give an opinion

D. to give information

Unit 12 Test

🎧 LISTENING I

(Tracks 69–70) **You will hear a question. Then you will hear a conversation. After that, you will hear the question again and three choices. What is the correct answer: A, B, or C?**

1. A. the rooms inside the White House
   B. the White House gardens
   C. the Washington Monument

2. A. freeing the slaves before the Civil War
   B. freeing the slaves during the Civil War
   C. getting killed in office

🎧 LISTENING II

(Tracks 71–72) **You will hear the first part of a conversation. To finish the conversation, listen and choose the correct answer: A, B, or C.**

3. A. They make the laws for the country.
   B. They decide whether laws follow the Constitution.
   C. The Supreme Court is one branch of the government.

4. A. Doesn't Chinatown have any good restaurants?
   B. What do you like about the restaurants there?
   C. OK. I'll try another place, then.

🎧 LISTENING III

(Tracks 73–74) **You will hear a conversation. Then you will hear three sentences. Which sentence is true: A, B, or C?**

5. A. George Washington was the fifth president.
   B. George Washington made his own money.
   C. George Washington became president in 1789.

6. A. Thomas Jefferson was the first president.
   B. Thomas Jefferson did not win the election in 1801.
   C. Thomas Jefferson was the third president.

LIFE SKILLS

Read the map on the next page. Then answer the questions. What is the correct answer: A, B, C, or D?

7. You are at Farragut West. You want to fly out of Dulles Airport. How do you get there?

   A. Take the metro west to Rosslyn, then take a bus.

   B. Take the metro east to Rosslyn, then take a bus.

   C. Take the metro west to Rosslyn. The airport is right there.

   D. Take a bus to the metro, then get on the orange line.

8. Which line takes you to both the Pentagon and the Smithsonian?

   A. the red line

   B. the yellow line

   C. the blue line

   D. the orange line

9. You are at Union Station. You want to go to the Pentagon. What is a transfer station where can you change for the yellow line?

   A. Judiciary Square

   B. Gallery Place

   C. Archives-Navy Memorial

   D. L' Enfant Plaza

10. You are at Union Station. You want to visit Arlington Cemetery. What's the fastest way to get there?

    A. Take the red line to Gallery Place, then transfer to the yellow line.

    B. Take the red line to Gallery Place, then transfer to the green line.

    C. Take the red line to Metro Center, then transfer to the orange line.

    D. Take the red line to Metro Center, then transfer to the blue line.

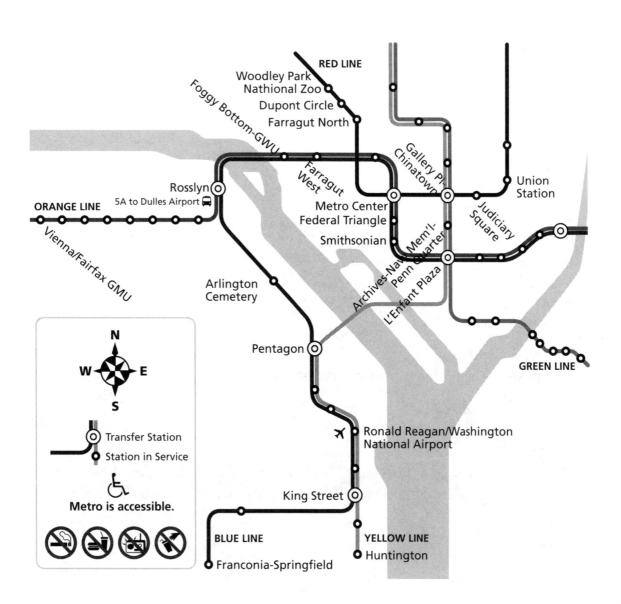

RED LINE

Woodley Park
Nathional Zoo

Dupont Circle

Farragut North

Foggy Bottom-GWU

Farragut West

Gallery Pl.-Chinatown

Union Station

Judiciary Square

Rosslyn

5A to Dulles Airport

ORANGE LINE

Metro Center
Federal Triangle

Smithsonian

Archives-Navy Mem'l-Penn Quarter

Vienna/Fairfax GMU

Arlington Cemetery

L'Enfant Plaza

Pentagon

GREEN LINE

N
W   E
S

Transfer Station

Station in Service

Metro is accessible.

Ronald Reagan/Washington
National Airport

King Street

YELLOW LINE

BLUE LINE

Huntington

Franconia-Springfield

GRAMMAR

Complete each conversation. What is the correct answer: A, B, or C?

11. **A:** Why is it so difficult to get a hotel room in Washington right now?

    B: Because the Cherry Blossom Festival is going on. It's _____ time of the year.

    A. the most crowded

    B. the crowded

    C. more crowded

12. **A:** I don't think I can walk up the Washington Monument. There are 897 steps!

    B: Yes, it's _____ monuments in the United States.

    A. the tallest

    B. one of the tallest

    C. most of the tall

13. **A:** Which president's wife was _____?

    B: I'm not sure. There were many famous first ladies.

    A. the famous

    B. one of the famous

    C. the most famous

14. **A:** My favorite place to go is Roosevelt Island. It's a big nature reserve on the Potomac River.

    B: Wow! I've never heard of it. It must be _____ kept secret in Washington.

    A. the best

    B. one of the best

    C. the good

15. **A:** Is Washington, D.C. _____ city in the United States?

    B: No, St. Augustine, Florida, is.

    A. the oldest

    B. one of the oldest

    C. most of the oldest

16. A: Where is the White House?

    B: It _____ at 1600 Pennsylvania Avenue.

    A. are located

    B. locates

    C. is located

17. A: Which president's face _____ on the twenty-dollar bill?

    B: Andrew Jackson, the seventh president.

    A. is printed

    B. are printed

    C. is printing

18. A: Where does Washington, D.C. have its fireworks?

    B: The fireworks _____ on the National Mall.

    A. is held

    B. are held

    C. held

19. A: Which place is the most popular to visit in Washington?

    B: I'm not sure, but my book says the White House _____ by more than one million visitors a year.

    A. are visiting

    B. is visited

    C. visits

20. A: What does the president use the Oval Office for?

    B: The Oval Office _____ for meeting with officials of other countries.

    A. is used

    B. are using

    C. are used

21. **A:** When was the Lincoln Memorial built? Right after the Civil War?
   B: No, it _____ until 1910.

   A. isn't built
   B. wasn't built
   C. weren't built

22. **A:** Many places _____ after George Washington, including Washington State, 121 towns, 7 mountains, 10 lakes, and 9 colleges.
   B: There are a lot of streets with his name, too, right?

   A. were named
   B. is named
   C. was named

23. **A:** How was President Lincoln killed?
   B: He was _____ while he was watching a play at a theater.

   A. shoots
   B. shot
   C. shooting

24. **A:** Which president served the most terms?
   B: President Franklin D. Roosevelt _____ four times.

   A. was elected
   B. is elected
   C. be elected

25. **A:** Who was the first Catholic president?
   B: President John F. Kennedy. He _____ in Massachusetts to a large Irish Catholic family.

   A. is born
   B. was born
   C. were born

VOCABULARY

Read. What is the correct answer: A, B, C, or D?

26. Many art treasures are stored in _____.

    A. the Pentagon

    B. the National Air and Space Museum

    C. the Smithsonian American Art Museum

    D. the Supreme Court

27. This part of the United States government takes care of its financial business: _____.

    A. the Pentagon

    B. the U.S. Treasury

    C. the Jefferson Memorial

    D. the Supreme Court

28. At _____, laws are written.

    A. the White House

    B. the Supreme Court

    C. the Capitol

    D. the Pentagon

29. At _____, 23,000 employees help keep the United States safe. There are offices for the Army, Navy, and Air Force, among others.

    A. the Pentagon

    B. the Supreme Court

    C. the U.S. Treasury

    D. the Lincoln Memorial

READING

Read. What is the correct answer: A, B, C, or D?

George Washington is one of the most loved presidents in the United States. His many qualities made him a special individual and a perfect choice to be the first president.

Washington was born in 1732 in Virginia. He was a farmer who joined the Virginia Militia (army) in 1752 when America went to war with France. He was a good fighter. When he was 43 years old, fighting started between America and Britain. George became the leader of the army and helped America win the Revolutionary War. After the war, Washington wanted to go back to his farm. But he was elected president of the United States in 1789 instead.

Washington served two terms as president, until 1797. He refused to be president a third time because he did not want to have power like a king. Washington was known for his fairness. He believed that a person's religion did not matter as long as the person was a good citizen. And although he owned slaves, he wrote in 1786 that slavery was wrong and that it should end. When Washington died, he freed all of his slaves in his will.

30. What is the main idea of the article?

A. George Washington freed his slaves.

B. George Washington was a great military leader.

C. George Washington was very fair.

D. George Washington was a remarkable individual to be president.

31. When did George Washington become president?

A. 1752

B. 1789

C. 1797

D. 1786

32. Why didn't George Washington want to be president a third time?

A. He was tired from two terms in office.

B. He preferred farming to being president.

C. He did not want to rule the United States like a king.

D. He thought Thomas Jefferson would be a better president.

33. What was one reason George Washington was considered fair?

A. He thought people of all religions could be good U.S. citizens.

B. He freed his slaves in his will.

C. He freed the slaves after the Revolutionary War.

D. He thought all Christians could be good U.S. citizens.

Future 3
Unit Test Answer Sheet

① _____
    Last Name   First Name   Middle

② _____
    Teacher's Name

TEST

1 Ⓐ Ⓑ Ⓒ Ⓓ
2 Ⓐ Ⓑ Ⓒ Ⓓ
3 Ⓐ Ⓑ Ⓒ Ⓓ
4 Ⓐ Ⓑ Ⓒ Ⓓ
5 Ⓐ Ⓑ Ⓒ Ⓓ
6 Ⓐ Ⓑ Ⓒ Ⓓ
7 Ⓐ Ⓑ Ⓒ Ⓓ
8 Ⓐ Ⓑ Ⓒ Ⓓ
9 Ⓐ Ⓑ Ⓒ Ⓓ
10 Ⓐ Ⓑ Ⓒ Ⓓ
11 Ⓐ Ⓑ Ⓒ Ⓓ
12 Ⓐ Ⓑ Ⓒ Ⓓ
13 Ⓐ Ⓑ Ⓒ Ⓓ
14 Ⓐ Ⓑ Ⓒ Ⓓ
15 Ⓐ Ⓑ Ⓒ Ⓓ
16 Ⓐ Ⓑ Ⓒ Ⓓ
17 Ⓐ Ⓑ Ⓒ Ⓓ
18 Ⓐ Ⓑ Ⓒ Ⓓ
19 Ⓐ Ⓑ Ⓒ Ⓓ
20 Ⓐ Ⓑ Ⓒ Ⓓ
21 Ⓐ Ⓑ Ⓒ Ⓓ
22 Ⓐ Ⓑ Ⓒ Ⓓ
23 Ⓐ Ⓑ Ⓒ Ⓓ
24 Ⓐ Ⓑ Ⓒ Ⓓ
25 Ⓐ Ⓑ Ⓒ Ⓓ
26 Ⓐ Ⓑ Ⓒ Ⓓ
27 Ⓐ Ⓑ Ⓒ Ⓓ
28 Ⓐ Ⓑ Ⓒ Ⓓ
29 Ⓐ Ⓑ Ⓒ Ⓓ
30 Ⓐ Ⓑ Ⓒ Ⓓ
31 Ⓐ Ⓑ Ⓒ Ⓓ
32 Ⓐ Ⓑ Ⓒ Ⓓ
33 Ⓐ Ⓑ Ⓒ Ⓓ

Directions for marking answers

- Use a No. 2 pencil. Do NOT use ink.
- Make dark marks and bubble in your answers completely.
- If you change an answer, erase your first mark completely.

Right
Ⓐ ⬤B Ⓒ Ⓓ

Wrong
Ⓐ ⊗ Ⓒ Ⓓ
Ⓐ Ⓑ Ⓒ Ⓓ

③ **STUDENT IDENTIFICATION**

0	0	0	0	0	0	0	0	0
1	1	1	1	1	1	1	1	1
2	2	2	2	2	2	2	2	2
3	3	3	3	3	3	3	3	3
4	4	4	4	4	4	4	4	4
5	5	5	5	5	5	5	5	5
6	6	6	6	6	6	6	6	6
7	7	7	7	7	7	7	7	7
8	8	8	8	8	8	8	8	8
9	9	9	9	9	9	9	9	9

Is this your Social Security number?
Yes ☐ No ☐

④ **TEST DATE**

MM	D	D	Y	Y
Jan	0	0	200	9
Feb	1	1	201	0
Mar	2	2	201	1
Apr	3	3	201	2
May		4	201	3
Jun		5	201	4
Jul		6	201	5
Aug		7	201	6
Sep		8	201	7
Oct		9	201	8
Nov				
Dec				

⑤ **CLASS NUMBER**

0	0	0	0	0	0	0	0
1	1	1	1	1	1	1	1
2	2	2	2	2	2	2	2
3	3	3	3	3	3	3	3
4	4	4	4	4	4	4	4
5	5	5	5	5	5	5	5
6	6	6	6	6	6	6	6
7	7	7	7	7	7	7	7
8	8	8	8	8	8	8	8
9	9	9	9	9	9	9	9

⑥ **RAW SCORE**

0	0
1	1
2	2
3	3
4	4
5	5
6	6
7	7
8	8
9	9

Unit 1 Test Answer Key

#	ANSWERS	LESSON/PAGE	OBJECTIVE
1	A **B** C D	5/p. 14	Understand a conversation about holidays and celebrations
2	A B **C** D	2/p. 8	Understand a conversation with small talk
3	A **B** C D	8/p. 20	Understand a conversation comparing your life now and in the past
4	**A** B C D	8/p. 20	Understand a conversation comparing your life now and in the past
5	A B **C** D	2/p. 8	Understand a conversation with small talk
6	A B **C** D	2/p. 8	Understand a conversation with small talk
7	A **B** C D	7/p. 18	Follow a recipe
8	A **B** C D	7/p. 18	Follow a recipe
9	**A** B C D	7/p. 18	Follow a recipe
10	A **B** C D	7/p. 18	Follow a recipe
11	A **B** C D	3/p. 10	Simple present
12	A B **C** D	3/p. 10	Simple present
13	**A** B C D	3/p. 10	Simple present
14	A B **C** D	3/p. 10	Simple present
15	A **B** C D	3/p. 10	Simple present
16	**A** B C D	6/p. 16	Quantifiers
17	**A** B C D	6/p. 16	Quantifiers
18	A B **C** D	6/p. 16	Quantifiers
19	A **B** C D	6/p. 16	Quantifiers
20	A B **C** D	6/p. 16	Quantifiers
21	A B **C** D	9/p. 22	*Used to*
22	A **B** C D	9/p. 22	*Used to*
23	A **B** C D	9/p. 22	*Used to*
24	**A** B C D	9/p. 22	*Used to*
25	A **B** C D	9/p. 22	*Used to*
26	A **B** C D	1/p. 2	Vocabulary
27	A B C **D**	1/p. 2	Vocabulary
28	**A** B C D	1/p. 2	Vocabulary
29	A B **C** D	1/p. 2	Vocabulary
30	A B **C** D	4/p. 12	Identify the main idea
31	A B C **D**	4/p. 12	Understand details
32	A **B** C D	4/p. 12	Understand details
33	A B **C** D	4/p. 12	Identify the main idea

Please see reverse for test audio script.

Unit 1 Test Audio Script

Listening I (Tracks 3–4) Page 1.

1. What does the woman do on Independence Day?
   F: My favorite holiday is Independence Day.
   M: What do you do on that day?
   F: We invite our friends over and have a big barbecue. Then we watch fireworks at the park.

   What does the woman do on Independence Day?

2. What does the man do for fun?
   F: What do you do for fun?
   M: I like to play basketball with my friends. How about you?
   F: I like to go swimming at the beach.

   What does the man do for fun?

Listening II (Tracks 5–6) Page 1.

3. M: Ying, do you want to go to the movies tomorrow?
   F: I can't. I have to work.
   M: But you usually have Fridays off.

4. F: Levi, what are you planning to do for New Year's Eve?
   M: Oh, I think I'll stay home this year.
   F: Oh, I thought you liked to go out.

Listening III (Tracks 7–8) Page 1.

5. F: Do you live near school?
   M: No. I live in Central City.

   Which sentence is true?

6. M: Do you play soccer on Sundays?
   F: No. My team plays on Saturdays.

   Which sentence is true?

Unit 2 Test Answer Key

	ANSWERS	LESSON/PAGE	OBJECTIVE
1	Ⓐ Ⓑ **Ⓒ** Ⓓ	2/p. 28	Understand a conversation about going back to school
2	Ⓐ **Ⓑ** Ⓒ Ⓓ	2/p. 28	Understand a conversation about going back to school
3	Ⓐ Ⓑ **Ⓒ** Ⓓ	5/p. 34	Understand a conversation about looking for a better job
4	**Ⓐ** Ⓑ Ⓒ Ⓓ	5/p. 34	Understand a conversation about looking for a better job
5	Ⓐ Ⓑ **Ⓒ** Ⓓ	9/p. 41	Understand a conversation about community services
6	Ⓐ **Ⓑ** Ⓒ Ⓓ	9/p. 41	Understand a conversation about community services
7	Ⓐ Ⓑ Ⓒ **Ⓓ**	7/p. 38	Set goals
8	**Ⓐ** Ⓑ Ⓒ Ⓓ	7/p. 38	Set goals
9	Ⓐ **Ⓑ** Ⓒ Ⓓ	7/p. 38	Set goals
10	Ⓐ Ⓑ **Ⓒ** Ⓓ	7/p. 38	Set goals
11	**Ⓐ** Ⓑ Ⓒ Ⓓ	3/p. 30	*Will/will probably/might*
12	Ⓐ **Ⓑ** Ⓒ Ⓓ	3/p. 30	*Will/will probably/might*
13	**Ⓐ** Ⓑ Ⓒ Ⓓ	3/p. 30	*Will/will probably/might*
14	Ⓐ Ⓑ **Ⓒ** Ⓓ	3/p. 30	*Will/will probably/might*
15	Ⓐ **Ⓑ** Ⓒ Ⓓ	3/p. 30	*Will/will probably/might*
16	**Ⓐ** Ⓑ Ⓒ Ⓓ	6/p. 36	The future with *be going to*
17	Ⓐ Ⓑ **Ⓒ** Ⓓ	6/p. 36	The future with *be going to*
18	**Ⓐ** Ⓑ Ⓒ Ⓓ	6/p. 36	The future with *be going to*
19	Ⓐ **Ⓑ** Ⓒ Ⓓ	6/p. 36	The future with *be going to*
20	Ⓐ Ⓑ **Ⓒ** Ⓓ	6/p. 36	The future with *be going to*
21	**Ⓐ** Ⓑ Ⓒ Ⓓ	10/p. 42	Present continuous for the future
22	Ⓐ **Ⓑ** Ⓒ Ⓓ	10/p. 42	Present continuous for the future
23	**Ⓐ** Ⓑ Ⓒ Ⓓ	10/p. 42	Present continuous for the future
24	Ⓐ Ⓑ **Ⓒ** Ⓓ	10/p. 42	Present continuous for the future
25	Ⓐ **Ⓑ** Ⓒ Ⓓ	10/p. 42	Present continuous for the future
26	Ⓐ Ⓑ **Ⓒ** Ⓓ	1/p. 46	Vocabulary
27	Ⓐ Ⓑ Ⓒ **Ⓓ**	1/p. 26	Vocabulary
28	Ⓐ Ⓑ **Ⓒ** Ⓓ	1/p. 26	Vocabulary
29	Ⓐ **Ⓑ** Ⓒ Ⓓ	1/p. 26	Vocabulary
30	Ⓐ Ⓑ **Ⓒ** Ⓓ	4/p. 32	Identify the main idea
31	Ⓐ Ⓑ Ⓒ **Ⓓ**	4/p. 32	Understand details
32	Ⓐ Ⓑ Ⓒ **Ⓓ**	4/p. 32	Identify the main idea
33	Ⓐ Ⓑ **Ⓒ** Ⓓ	4/p. 32	Understand details

Please see reverse for test audio script.

Unit 2 Test Audio Script

Listening I (Tracks 9–10) Page 8.

1. What is the woman going to do?
   F: I'm going to take night classes this spring.
   M: Yeah? Where?
   F: At Cedar Falls Community College.

   What is the woman going to do?

2. What does the man want?
   M: I'm taking math classes after work.
   F: Oh really? I took classes at night and I got a certificate in accounting! Now I have a new job, and I love it!
   M: That's great! I'm taking classes because I've decided to get an associate's degree.

   What does the man want?

Listening II (Tracks 11–12) Page 8.

3. **M:** So, Anh, how's work going?
   F: Not so good. I have to find a new job. I need to make more money.
   M: I see. Well, you can start by looking online. Let me know if you need help.

4. **F:** Ugh, I need a new job.
   M: Why, what's the matter?
   F: Well, I work nights, but I'm always tired in the morning.

Listening III (Tracks 13–14) Page 8.

5. **M:** Are you coming to the meeting at the Community Center?
   F: I'll try to come. What's it about?

   Which sentence is true?

6. **F:** I'm going to the Community Center this Sunday. We're going to talk about how to raise money to build a new park.
   M: We really need a park. I'll be there, too!

   Which sentence is true?

Unit 3 Test Answer Key

	ANSWERS	LESSON/PAGE	OBJECTIVE
1	Ⓐ Ⓑ Ⓒ Ⓓ	2/p. 48	Understand a conversation about problems at school
2	Ⓐ Ⓑ Ⓒ Ⓓ	2/p. 48	Understand a conversation about problems at school
3	Ⓐ Ⓑ Ⓒ Ⓓ	7/p. 55	Understand a conversation about dealing with bullies
4	Ⓐ Ⓑ Ⓒ Ⓓ	7/p. 55	Understand a conversation about dealing with bullies
5	Ⓐ Ⓑ Ⓒ Ⓓ	9/p. 60	Understand a conversation about helping children continue their education
6	Ⓐ Ⓑ Ⓒ Ⓓ	9/p. 60	Understand a conversation about helping children continue their education
7	Ⓐ Ⓑ Ⓒ Ⓓ	8/p. 58	Read a report card
8	Ⓐ Ⓑ Ⓒ Ⓓ	8/p. 58	Read a report card
9	Ⓐ Ⓑ Ⓒ Ⓓ	8/p. 58	Read a report card
10	Ⓐ Ⓑ Ⓒ Ⓓ	8/p. 58	Read a report card
11	Ⓐ Ⓑ Ⓒ Ⓓ	3/p. 50	Inseparable and separable phrasal verbs
12	Ⓐ Ⓑ Ⓒ Ⓓ	3/p. 50	Inseparable and separable phrasal verbs
13	Ⓐ Ⓑ Ⓒ Ⓓ	3/p. 50	Inseparable and separable phrasal verbs
14	Ⓐ Ⓑ Ⓒ Ⓓ	3/p. 50	Inseparable and separable phrasal verbs
15	Ⓐ Ⓑ Ⓒ Ⓓ	3/p. 50	Inseparable and separable phrasal verbs
16	Ⓐ Ⓑ Ⓒ Ⓓ	7/p. 56	Simple past review: Regular and irregular verbs
17	Ⓐ Ⓑ Ⓒ Ⓓ	7/p. 56	Simple past review: Regular and irregular verbs
18	Ⓐ Ⓑ Ⓒ Ⓓ	7/p. 56	Simple past review: Regular and irregular verbs
19	Ⓐ Ⓑ Ⓒ Ⓓ	7/p. 56	Simple past review: *Wh-* questions
20	Ⓐ Ⓑ Ⓒ Ⓓ	7/p. 56	Simple past review: Regular and irregular verbs
21	Ⓐ Ⓑ Ⓒ Ⓓ	10/p. 62	Help children continue their education
22	Ⓐ Ⓑ Ⓒ Ⓓ	10/p. 62	Help children continue their education
23	Ⓐ Ⓑ Ⓒ Ⓓ	10/p. 62	Help children continue their education
24	Ⓐ Ⓑ Ⓒ Ⓓ	10/p. 62	Help children continue their education
25	Ⓐ Ⓑ Ⓒ Ⓓ	10/p. 62	Help children continue their education
26	Ⓐ Ⓑ Ⓒ Ⓓ	1/p. 46	Vocabulary
27	Ⓐ Ⓑ Ⓒ Ⓓ	1/p. 46	Vocabulary
28	Ⓐ Ⓑ Ⓒ Ⓓ	1/p. 46	Vocabulary
29	Ⓐ Ⓑ Ⓒ Ⓓ	1/p. 46	Vocabulary
30	Ⓐ Ⓑ Ⓒ Ⓓ	4/p. 52	Identify the main idea
31	Ⓐ Ⓑ Ⓒ Ⓓ	4/p. 52	Understand details
32	Ⓐ Ⓑ Ⓒ Ⓓ	4/p. 52	Understand details
33	Ⓐ Ⓑ Ⓒ Ⓓ	4/p. 52	Understand details

Please see reverse for test audio script.

Unit 3 Test Audio Script

Listening I (Tracks 15–16) Page 15.

1. What does Joey need to do?
   F: Joey, did you do your homework?
   M: Uhh . . . I'll do it later, mom. I'm watching TV right now.
   F: I don't think so. Please go to your room and do it now.

   What does Joey need to do?

2. What is Samantha's problem?
   M: How was school today, Samantha?
   F: Terrible! I have a lot of homework to do.
   M: Well, go ahead and start, and I'll help you in a little bit.

   What is Samantha's problem?

Listening II (Tracks 17–18) Page 15.

3. **F:** Oh, what happened to you today?
   M: A kid in my class hit me after lunch.
   F: Tell me why.

4. **F:** I called Jonathan's teacher today.
   M: Why, what's the matter?
   F: Well, Jonathan told me that some kids are making fun of him every day.

Listening III (Tracks 19–20) Page 15.

5. **M:** What classes should my son take in high school next year?
   F: I don't know. Maybe you should talk to the counselor.

   Which sentence is true?

6. **F:** My daughter doesn't like math, and she's getting bad grades.
   M: You could take her to the learning center after school. They have people there who can help her.

   Which sentence is true?

Unit 4 Test Answer Key

	ANSWERS	LESSON/PAGE	OBJECTIVE
1	A B **C** D	2/p. 68	Understand a conversation about work experience
2	A B **C** D	2/p. 68	Understand a conversation about work experience
3	**A** B C D	2/p. 68	Understand a conversation about work experience
4	A **B** C D	5/p. 74	Understand a conversation describing work history
5	A **B** C D	5/p. 74	Understand a conversation describing work history
6	A **B** C D	10/p. 82	Understand a conversation about positive work behavior
7	A B **C** D	4/p. 72	Read a job application
8	A B **C** D	4/p. 72	Read a job application
9	A B **C** D	4/p. 72	Read a job application
10	A **B** C D	4/p. 72	Read a job application
11	**A** B C D	3/p. 70	Present perfect: *Yes/No* questions with *ever* and *never*
12	A B **C** D	3/p. 70	Present perfect: *Yes/No* questions with *ever* and *never*
13	**A** B C D	3/p. 70	Present perfect: *Yes/No* questions with *ever* and *never*
14	A B **C** D	3/p. 70	Present perfect: *Yes/No* questions with *ever* and *never*
15	**A** B C D	3/p. 70	Present perfect: *Yes/No* questions with *ever* and *never*
16	A **B** C D	6/p. 76	Present perfect: Statements with *for* and *since*
17	**A** B C D	6/p. 76	Present perfect: Statements with *for* and *since*
18	A B **C** D	6/p. 76	Present perfect: Statements with *for* and *since*
19	A **B** C D	6/p. 76	Present perfect: Statements with *for* and *since*
20	A B **C** D	6/p. 76	Present perfect: Statements with *for* and *since*
21	**A** B C D	10/p. 82	*It + Be + Adjective + Infinitive*
22	A **B** C D	10/p. 82	*It + Be + Adjective + Infinitive*
23	A **B** C D	10/p. 82	*It + Be + Adjective + Infinitive*
24	A B **C** D	10/p. 82	*It + Be + Adjective + Infinitive*
25	**A** B C D	10/p. 82	*It + Be + Adjective + Infinitive*
26	A B C **D**	1/p. 66	Vocabulary
27	A **B** C D	1/p. 66	Vocabulary
28	A B **C** D	1/p. 66	Vocabulary
29	A B C **D**	1/p. 66	Vocabulary
30	**A** B C D	4/p. 72	Identify the main idea
31	A B C **D**	4/p. 72	Understand details
32	A B **C** D	4/p. 72	Understand details
33	**A** B C D	4/p. 72	Make inferences

Please see reverse for test audio script.

Unit 4 Test Audio Script

Listening I (Tracks 21–22) Page 22.

1. How long has the man worked at the store?
   F: So, you've been an assistant manager for two years?
   M: Yes, that's right. And I've worked at the store for five years.
   F: OK, great. Have you ever worked at night?

   How long has the man worked at the store?

2. Where has the woman worked?
   M: Have you ever worked at a bank?
   F: No, but I have worked with money. I used to work at a restaurant.
   M: I see. Well, tell me more about that job.

   Where has the woman worked?

Listening II (Tracks 23–24) Page 22.

3. **F:** Where did you drive a truck?
   M: In San Francisco. I delivered boxes.
   F: Have you ever been in a driving accident?

4. **F:** Can you tell me about your experience?
   M: Sure. I've been a restaurant manager for three years.
   F: So, why do you want to leave that job?

Listening III (Tracks 25–26) Page 22.

5. **M:** How did you find out about this job?
   F: First, a friend told me. Then, I also found it on the Internet.

   Which sentence is true?

6. **F:** My boss is always yelling at me.
   M: That's too bad. It's important for managers to be polite.

   Which sentence is true?

Unit 5 Test Answer Key

	ANSWERS	LESSON/PAGE	OBJECTIVE
1	A B **C** D	2/p. 88	Understand a conversation about following instructions at an airport
2	A **B** C D	2/p. 88	Understand a conversation about following instructions at an airport
3	A B **C** D	5/p. 94	Understand a conversation about travel arrangements
4	A **B** C D	5/p. 94	Understand a conversation about travel arrangements
5	**A** B C D	9/p. 101	Understand a conversation about delays and cancellations
6	**A** B C D	9/p. 101	Understand a conversation about delays and cancellations
7	A **B** C D	4/p. 92	Read screen instructions
8	A B C **D**	4/p. 92	Read screen instructions
9	A **B** C D	4/p. 92	Read screen instructions
10	**A** B C D	4/p. 92	Read screen instructions
11	A **B** C D	3/p. 90	*Can/Could/Be able to:* Affirmative and negative
12	A B **C** D	3/p. 90	*Can/Could/Be able to:* Affirmative and negative
13	**A** B C D	3/p. 90	*Can/Could/Be able to:* Affirmative and negative
14	A B **C** D	3/p. 90	*Can/Could/Be able to:* Affirmative and negative
15	A **B** C D	3/p. 90	*Can/Could/Be able to:* Affirmative and negative
16	A B **C** D	6/p. 96	Possessive adjectives and pronouns
17	A **B** C D	6/p. 96	Possessive adjectives and pronouns
18	**A** B C D	6/p. 96	Possessive adjectives and pronouns
19	A B **C** D	6/p. 96	Possessive adjectives and pronouns
20	A **B** C D	6/p. 96	Possessive adjectives and pronouns
21	A **B** C D	10/p. 102	Make polite requests and ask for permission
22	**A** B C D	10/p. 102	Make polite requests and ask for permission
23	A B **C** D	10/p. 102	Make polite requests and ask for permission
24	**A** B C D	10/p. 102	Make polite requests and ask for permission
25	A **B** C D	10/p. 102	Make polite requests and ask for permission
26	A **B** C D	1/p. 86	Vocabulary
27	A B **C** D	1/p. 86	Vocabulary
28	A **B** C D	1/p. 86	Vocabulary
29	A B C **D**	1/p. 86	Vocabulary
30	A B **C** D	7/p. 98	Identify the main idea
31	A **B** C D	7/p. 98	Understand details
32	**A** B C D	7/p. 98	Understand details
33	A B C **D**	7/p. 98	Make inferences

Please see reverse for test audio script.

Unit 5 Test Audio Script

Listening I (Tracks 27–28) Page 29.

1. What is the problem?
   F: I'm sorry, but you can't bring that bag onto the flight. It won't fit in the overhead bin.
   M: Oh? Can I check it with my luggage?
   F: Yes, we can take care of that for you. Here's a luggage tag.

   What is the problem?

2. What does security need to see?
   M: I need to see your photo ID and your boarding pass.
   F: Here you go.
   M: Thank you. Have a nice flight.

   What does security need to see?

Listening II (Tracks 29–30) Page 29.

3. **M:** Hey, can you pick me up? I missed the bus.
   F: Yeah, sure. Where are you?
   M: I'm at First and Grand. Can you come now?

4. **M:** Call me when you land.
   F: OK. Can you meet me at the baggage claim?
   M: Sure. Do you have a lot of luggage?

Listening III (Tracks 31–32) Page 29.

5. **M:** Hey, Mary. Guess what? My flight got canceled. It's snowing here in Chicago. I have to stay for another night.
   F: Oh, no! Well, I hope you can get a flight out in the morning.

   Which sentence is true?

6. **M:** Did you hear the announcement? Our gate has changed. We need to go to Gate 13.
   F: Oh. I thought the announcer said Gate 30. Let's check the screen.

   Which sentence is true?

Unit 6 Test Answer Key

	ANSWERS	LESSON/PAGE	OBJECTIVE
1	Ⓐ (B) Ⓒ Ⓓ	2/p. 108	Understand a conversation about product defects
2	(A) Ⓑ Ⓒ Ⓓ	2/p. 108	Understand a conversation about product defects
3	Ⓐ (B) Ⓒ Ⓓ	5/p. 114	Understand a conversation about problems with cell phone service
4	Ⓐ Ⓑ (C) Ⓓ	5/p. 114	Understand a conversation about cell phone service
5	(A) Ⓑ Ⓒ Ⓓ	8/p. 120	Understand a conversation about making an exchange
6	Ⓐ (B) Ⓒ Ⓓ	8/p. 120	Understand a conversation about making an exchange
7	(A) Ⓑ Ⓒ Ⓓ	7/p. 118	Read sales ads and rebates
8	Ⓐ Ⓑ (C) Ⓓ	7/p. 118	Read sales ads and rebates
9	Ⓐ Ⓑ Ⓒ (D)	7/p. 118	Read sales ads and rebates
10	(A) Ⓑ Ⓒ Ⓓ	7/p. 118	Read sales ads and rebates
11	(A) Ⓑ Ⓒ Ⓓ	3/p. 110	Noun clauses
12	(A) Ⓑ Ⓒ Ⓓ	3/p. 110	Noun clauses
13	Ⓐ Ⓑ (C) Ⓓ	3/p. 110	Noun clauses
14	(A) Ⓑ Ⓒ Ⓓ	3/p. 110	Noun clauses
15	Ⓐ (B) Ⓒ Ⓓ	3/p. 110	Noun clauses
16	(A) Ⓑ Ⓒ Ⓓ	6/p. 116	Comparison of adjectives
17	Ⓐ (B) Ⓒ Ⓓ	6/p. 116	Comparison of adjectives
18	Ⓐ (B) Ⓒ Ⓓ	6/p. 116	Comparison of adjectives
19	Ⓐ Ⓑ (C) Ⓓ	6/p. 116	Comparison of adjectives
20	(A) Ⓑ Ⓒ Ⓓ	6/p. 116	Comparison of adjectives
21	Ⓐ Ⓑ (C) Ⓓ	9/p. 122	As . . . as with adjectives
22	(A) Ⓑ Ⓒ Ⓓ	9/p. 122	As . . . as with adjectives
23	Ⓐ (B) Ⓒ Ⓓ	9/p. 122	As . . . as with adjectives
24	Ⓐ Ⓑ (C) Ⓓ	9/p. 122	As . . . as with adjectives
25	(A) Ⓑ Ⓒ Ⓓ	9/p. 122	As . . . as with adjectives
26	Ⓐ Ⓑ Ⓒ (D)	1/p. 106	Vocabulary
27	(A) Ⓑ Ⓒ Ⓓ	1/p. 106	Vocabulary
28	Ⓐ Ⓑ (C) Ⓓ	1/p. 106	Vocabulary
29	Ⓐ (B) Ⓒ Ⓓ	1/p. 106	Vocabulary
30	Ⓐ Ⓑ (C) Ⓓ	4/p. 112	Identify the main idea
31	(A) Ⓑ Ⓒ Ⓓ	4/p. 112	Understand details
32	Ⓐ Ⓑ (C) Ⓓ	4/p. 112	Understand details
33	Ⓐ Ⓑ Ⓒ (D)	4/p. 112	Make inferences

Please see reverse for test audio script.

Unit 6 Test Audio Script

Listening I (Tracks 33–34) Page 36.

1. What's the problem?
   F: Ouch! I got zapped by the vacuum cleaner!
   M: Oh, no. Don't touch it again. Look at the cord; it's frayed.
   F: Oh, you're right. I see it now. Let's call the service number.

   What's the problem?

2. What does the man want to know?
   M: Honey, when did we buy this microwave?
   F: Why?
   M: Well, I think it's broken. Do you know if it's still under warranty?

   What does the man want to know?

Listening II (Tracks 35–36) Page 36.

3. **M:** Thank you for calling Sunphone. How can I help you?
   F: I have a problem with my last bill. I don't understand some of the charges.
   M: OK. I'm looking at your statement now. Tell me which charges you don't understand.

4. **M:** Thank you for calling Sunphone. How can I help you?
   F: I'd like to change my cell phone service plan.
   M: OK. Do you know which plan you want?

Listening III (Tracks 37–38) Page 36.

5. **M:** I'd like to return this remote control.
   F: Is there anything wrong with it?
   M: It doesn't work. I think it's broken.

   Which sentence is true?

6. **M:** Could I exchange this DVD player for a less expensive one?
   F: Sure. We can give you the difference in store credit.

   Which sentence is true?

Unit 7 Test Answer Key

	ANSWERS	LESSON/PAGE	OBJECTIVE
1	(A) (B) (C) (D)	2/p. 128	Understand a conversation about car maintenance
2	(A) (B) (C) (D)	5/p. 134	Understand a conversation about traffic accidents
3	(A) (B) (C) (D)	2/p. 128	Understand a conversation identifying parts of a car
4	(A) (B) (C) (D)	4/p. 132	Understand a conversation identifying parts of a car
5	(A) (B) (C) (D)	4/p. 132	Understand a conversation about traffic accidents
6	(A) (B) (C) (D)	6/p. 136	Understand a conversation about traffic accidents
7	(A) (B) (C) (D)	4/p. 132	Identify parts of a car
8	(A) (B) (C) (D)	4/p. 132	Identify parts of a car
9	(A) (B) (C) (D)	4/p. 132	Identify parts of a car
10	(A) (B) (C) (D)	4/p. 132	Identify parts of a car
11	(A) (B) (C) (D)	3/p. 130	*A, An, The*
12	(A) (B) (C) (D)	3/p. 130	*A, An, The*
13	(A) (B) (C) (D)	3/p. 130	*A, An, The*
14	(A) (B) (C) (D)	3/p. 130	*A, An, The*
15	(A) (B) (C) (D)	3/p. 130	*A, An, The*
16	(A) (B) (C) (D)	6/p. 136	Past continuous
17	(A) (B) (C) (D)	6/p. 136	Past continuous
18	(A) (B) (C) (D)	6/p. 136	Past continuous
19	(A) (B) (C) (D)	6/p. 136	Past continuous
20	(A) (B) (C) (D)	6/p. 136	Past continuous
21	(A) (B) (C) (D)	10/p. 142	Present time clauses
22	(A) (B) (C) (D)	10/p. 142	Present time clauses
23	(A) (B) (C) (D)	10/p. 142	Present time clauses
24	(A) (B) (C) (D)	10/p. 142	Present time clauses
25	(A) (B) (C) (D)	10/p. 142	Present time clauses
26	(A) (B) (C) (D)	1/p. 126	Vocabulary
27	(A) (B) (C) (D)	1/p. 126	Vocabulary
28	(A) (B) (C) (D)	1/p. 126	Vocabulary
29	(A) (B) (C) (D)	1/p. 126	Vocabulary
30	(A) (B) (C) (D)	7/p. 138	Identify the main idea
31	(A) (B) (C) (D)	7/p. 138	Understand details
32	(A) (B) (C) (D)	7/p. 138	Interpret charts
33	(A) (B) (C) (D)	7/p. 138	Make inferences

Please see reverse for test audio script.

Unit 7 Test Audio Script

Listening I (Tracks 39–40) Page 43.

1. What is the man going to do?
   F: I'd like an oil change. How much will that be?
   M: Well, do you want me to check the brakes or rotate the tires, too?
   F: No, thanks.
   M: OK, then it'll be $29.95.

   What is the man going to do?

2. What's the problem?
   M: May I see your license, registration, and insurance please?
   F: Of course, officer…. Here you are.
   M: Can you tell me what happened?
   F: I was driving in the right lane. I was going pretty slow. Suddenly a car came from the left, and it hit my car.

   What's the problem?

Listening II (Tracks 41–42) Page 43.

3. **F:** Where did you put the suitcases?

4. **M:** My car won't start.
   F: What's the problem?

Listening III (Tracks 43–44) Page 43.

5. **F:** I just heard the traffic report. There's a 15-minute delay on Route 25.
   M: What happened? Was there an accident?
   F: No, there's some construction that's causing a traffic jam.

   Which sentence is true?

6. **M:** Sorry I'm late. There was a lot of traffic.
   F: Oh? Was it because of the rain?
   M: No. There was an accident on the highway. Some drivers were rubbernecking to see what happened.

   Which sentence is true?

Unit 8 Test Answer Key

	ANSWERS	LESSON/PAGE	OBJECTIVE
1	Ⓐ Ⓑ **C** Ⓓ	2/p. 148	Understand a conversation about eating habits
2	Ⓐ Ⓑ **C** Ⓓ	2/p. 148	Understand a conversation about eating habits
3	Ⓐ **B** Ⓒ Ⓓ	5/p. 154	Understand a conversation about family health
4	**A** Ⓑ Ⓒ Ⓓ	8/p. 160	Understand a conversation about dental health
5	Ⓐ **B** Ⓒ Ⓓ	5/p. 154	Understand a conversation about family health
6	Ⓐ **B** Ⓒ Ⓓ	5/p. 154	Understand a conversation about family health
7	Ⓐ **B** Ⓒ Ⓓ	4/p. 152	Read a nutritional label
8	Ⓐ Ⓑ **C** Ⓓ	4/p. 152	Read a nutritional label
9	Ⓐ Ⓑ Ⓒ **D**	4/p. 152	Read a nutritional label
10	**A** Ⓑ Ⓒ Ⓓ	4/p. 152	Read a nutritional label
11	Ⓐ **B** Ⓒ Ⓓ	3/p. 150	Adverbs of frequency
12	Ⓐ Ⓑ **C** Ⓓ	3/p. 150	Adverbs of frequency
13	**A** Ⓑ Ⓒ Ⓓ	3/p. 150	Adverbs of frequency
14	Ⓐ Ⓑ **C** Ⓓ	3/p. 150	Adverbs of frequency
15	**A** Ⓑ Ⓒ Ⓓ	3/p. 150	Adverbs of frequency
16	**A** Ⓑ Ⓒ Ⓓ	6/p. 156	Verb + gerund as object
17	Ⓐ **B** Ⓒ Ⓓ	6/p. 156	Verb + gerund as object
18	Ⓐ Ⓑ **C** Ⓓ	6/p. 156	Verb + gerund as object
19	Ⓐ **B** Ⓒ Ⓓ	6/p. 156	Verb + gerund as object
20	**A** Ⓑ Ⓒ Ⓓ	6/p. 156	Verb + gerund as object
21	Ⓐ **B** Ⓒ Ⓓ	9/p. 162	Gerunds
22	**A** Ⓑ Ⓒ Ⓓ	9/p. 162	Gerunds
23	Ⓐ Ⓑ **C** Ⓓ	9/p. 162	Gerunds
24	**A** Ⓑ Ⓒ Ⓓ	9/p. 162	Gerunds
25	Ⓐ **B** Ⓒ Ⓓ	9/p. 162	Gerunds
26	Ⓐ Ⓑ Ⓒ **D**	1/p. 146	Vocabulary
27	Ⓐ Ⓑ **C** Ⓓ	1/p. 146	Vocabulary
28	**A** Ⓑ Ⓒ Ⓓ	1/p. 146	Vocabulary
29	Ⓐ **B** Ⓒ Ⓓ	1/p. 146	Vocabulary
30	Ⓐ Ⓑ **C** Ⓓ	7/p. 158	Identify the main idea
31	Ⓐ Ⓑ Ⓒ **D**	7/p. 158	Understand details
32	Ⓐ **B** Ⓒ Ⓓ	7/p. 158	Understand facts
33	**A** Ⓑ Ⓒ Ⓓ	7/p. 158	Understand opinions

Please see reverse for test audio script.

Unit 8 Test Audio Script

Listening I (Tracks 45–46) Page 50.

1. What does the woman usually have for a snack?
   M: What do you usually eat for a snack, Maria?
   F: Well, I like chips, but I'm trying not to eat a lot of salt. So I usually eat vegetables like carrots and celery.
   M: Oh. I only like vegetables with dip.

   What does the woman usually have for a snack?

2. Why does the woman skip meals?
   M: Beatriz, you shouldn't skip meals. Do you do that often?
   F: Well, sometimes I'm so busy taking care of my children that I forget to eat.
   M: Wow. I could *never* forget to eat! But sometimes I skip breakfast if I'm late to work.

   Why does the woman skip meals?

Listening II (Tracks 47–48) Page 50.

3. **M:** Here's the birthday cake. It looks delicious. And it's nut-free.
   F: Does it have milk in it?
   M: I don't know. Why?

4. **M:** Usually I brush my teeth two times a day.
   F: And how often do you floss?
   M: Oh, I don't know, maybe once a month.

Listening III (Tracks 49–50) Page 50.

5. **M:** There are many foods that have protein and are low in fat. For example, fish, turkey, and chicken.
   F: What about steak?

   Which sentence is true?

6. **F:** When can my daughter drink milk?
   M: She can drink whole milk when she is twelve months old. When she turns two, she can continue drinking whole milk or you can give her low-fat milk.

   Which sentence is true?

Unit 9 Test Answer Key

	ANSWERS	LESSON/PAGE	OBJECTIVE
1	A B **C** D	6/p. 175	Understand a conversation about expectations on the job
2	**A** B C D	6/p. 175	Understand a conversation about expectations on the job
3	A **B** C D	2/p. 168	Understand a conversation asking for clarification
4	**A** B C D	2/p. 168	Understand a conversation asking for clarification
5	A **B** C D	2/p. 168	Understand a conversation asking for clarification
6	**A** B C D	9/p. 180	Understand a conversation responding appropriately to correction
7	**A** B C D	8/p. 178	Identify safety hazards at work
8	A B C **D**	8/p. 178	Identify safety hazards at work
9	A B C **D**	8/p. 178	Identify safety hazards at work
10	A **B** C D	8/p. 178	Identify safety hazards at work
11	A **B** C D	3/p. 170	*One/ones*
12	**A** B C D	3/p. 170	*One/ones*
13	**A** B C D	3/p. 170	*One/ones*
14	**A** B C D	3/p. 170	*One/ones*
15	**A** B C D	3/p. 170	*One/ones*
16	**A** B C D	7/p. 176	Verb + object + infinitive
17	A **B** C D	7/p. 176	Verb + object + infinitive
18	**A** B C D	7/p. 176	Verb + object + infinitive
19	**A** B C D	7/p. 176	Verb + object + infinitive
20	**A** B C D	7/p. 176	Verb + object + infinitive
21	A B **C** D	10/p. 182	Reported speech: commands and requests with *tell/ask*
22	**A** B C D	10/p. 182	Reported speech: commands and requests with *tell/ask*
23	A B **C** D	10/p. 182	Reported speech: commands and requests with *tell/ask*
24	A B **C** D	10/p. 182	Reported speech: commands and requests with *tell/ask*
25	A **B** C D	10/p. 182	Reported speech: commands and requests with *tell/ask*
26	A B **C** D	1/p. 166	Vocabulary
27	A **B** C D	1/p. 166	Vocabulary
28	**A** B C D	1/p. 166	Vocabulary
29	A B C **D**	1/p. 166	Vocabulary
30	A B C **D**	4/p. 172	Identify the main idea
31	**A** B C D	4/p. 172	Understand details
32	**A** B C D	4/p. 172	Understand details
33	A **B** C D	4/p. 172	Understand details

Please see reverse for test audio script.

Unit 9 Test Audio Script

Listening I (Tracks 51–52) Page 57.

1. What is the man asking for?
   M: Ms. Li, could I speak to you for a minute?
   F: Sure, Roberto, what can I do for you?
   M: I was wondering if I could take next Friday off. My cousin from Florida is coming to visit.

   What is the man asking for?

2. What is the man asking for?
   M: Ana, I'm going to be in a meeting for several hours. Please don't interrupt me with any calls.
   F: OK.
   M: Just take a message and I'll call them back.

   What is the man asking for?

Listening II (Tracks 53–54) Page 57.

3. **F:** You said that the bus driver has to know all the city traffic rules and sometimes discipline children. Can you explain more?
   M: Yes. When you're driving the bus, you need to make sure that the children do not get into fights.
   F: How do I do that?

4. **M:** What do you need me to do next, Pamela?
   F: We need to bring down some large boxes from the top shelf. They have the new batch of medications.
   M: Which boxes do you need me to get?

Listening III (Tracks 55–56) Page 57.

5. **M:** Excuse me, Marjorie. Did you say the shipment is coming in on Thursday, January fifth, or on Friday?
   F: Let me check. Thursday. Wait. There is a note here that the shipment will be a day late. So I guess it will arrive on the sixth.

   Which sentence is true?

6. **F:** Hakkim, could I see you for a minute? Your coworker Adina says that you yelled at her. You know, we don't allow this at the company.
   M: I'm sorry, Marjorie. She was working slowly, and I lost my temper. I promise I won't yell at anyone again.

   Which sentence is true?

Unit 10 Test Answer Key

#	ANSWERS	LESSON/PAGE	OBJECTIVE
1	(A) **B** (C) (D)	2/p. 188	Understand a conversation about rescheduling a doctor's appointment
2	(A) (B) **C** (D)	5/p. 194	Understand a conversation about symptoms
3	**A** (B) (C) (D)	5/p. 194	Understand a conversation about symptoms
4	(A) (B) **C** (D)	5/p. 194	Understand a conversation about symptoms
5	(A) **B** (C) (D)	2/p. 188	Understand a conversation rescheduling a doctor's appointment
6	(A) (B) **C** (D)	5/p. 194	Understand a conversation about symptoms
7	(A) (B) **C** (D)	4/p. 192	Identify parts of the body
8	(A) **B** (C) (D)	4/p. 192	Identify parts of the body
9	(A) **B** (C) (D)	4/p. 192	Identify parts of the body
10	(A) (B) (C) **D**	4/p. 192	Identify parts of the body
11	(A) (B) (C) **D**	3/p. 190	Participial adjectives
12	**A** (B) (C) (D)	3/p. 190	Participial adjectives
13	(A) **B** (C) (D)	3/p. 190	Participial adjectives
14	(A) (B) **C** (D)	3/p. 190	Participial adjectives
15	**A** (B) (C) (D)	3/p. 190	Participial adjectives
16	**A** (B) (C) (D)	6/p. 196	Present perfect continuous
17	(A) (B) **C** (D)	6/p. 196	Present perfect continuous
18	**A** (B) (C) (D)	6/p. 196	Present perfect continuous
19	(A) (B) **C** (D)	6/p. 196	Present perfect continuous
20	(A) **B** (C) (D)	6/p. 196	Present perfect continuous
21	(A) (B) **C** (D)	10/p. 202	Preposition + gerund
22	(A) (B) **C** (D)	10/p. 202	Preposition + gerund
23	**A** (B) (C) (D)	10/p. 202	Preposition + gerund
24	(A) **B** (C) (D)	10/p. 202	Preposition + gerund
25	(A) (B) **C** (D)	10/p. 202	Preposition + gerund
26	(A) (B) (C) **D**	1/p. 186	Vocabulary
27	(A) (B) **C** (D)	1/p. 186	Vocabulary
28	**A** (B) (C) (D)	1/p. 186	Vocabulary
29	(A) **B** (C) (D)	1/p. 186	Vocabulary
30	(A) (B) **C** (D)	7/p. 198	Identify the main idea
31	(A) (B) (C) **D**	7/p. 198	Understand details
32	(A) (B) **C** (D)	7/p. 198	Interpret graphics
33	(A) **B** (C) (D)	7/p. 198	Make inferences

Please see reverse for test audio script.

Unit 10 Test Audio Script

Listening I (Tracks 57–58) Page 64.

1. What is the man doing?
   F: Hello, East Side Health Center.
   M: Yes, I have an appointment with Dr. Yin on Thursday, but I need to cancel. I have to work that day.
   F: OK. Would you like to come in another day?

   What is the man doing?

2. What are Mrs. Bailey's symptoms?
   M: So, Mrs. Bailey, how have you been feeling? Are you still having back pain and headaches?
   F: No, those went away. But I've been having terrible pain in my stomach. Sometimes I have nausea.
   M: Hmm. Let's start the examination. Please put on this gown.

   What are Mrs. Bailey's symptoms?

Listening II (Tracks 59–60) Page 64.

3. **M:** Good afternoon, Mrs. Martinez. I'm sorry to hear that you've been having headaches.
   F: Yes. My head hurts so much I can't think.
   M: It could be migraine headaches. Have you ever had them before?

4. **M:** How have you been feeling, Miss Garcia?
   F: Not so good. I've been having bad heartburn. Doctor Salik, what should I do?
   M: Try sleeping with two pillows. Keep your head raised. And try not to drink coffee or alcohol.

Listening III (Tracks 61–62) Page 64.

5. **M:** Hello, this is Yuan Deng. I want to make an appointment with Dr. Hops. Are there any openings on Thursday or Friday?
   F: I'm sorry. We're completely booked on Thursday. And we're closed this Friday.

   Which sentence is true?

6. **M:** Dr. Ruiz, I don't know what's wrong with me. I have to get up every night to go to the bathroom. And I've been feeling tired and weak.
   F: Hmm. I think we may need to run some blood tests.

   Which sentence is true?

Unit 11 Test Answer Key

	ANSWERS	LESSON/PAGE	OBJECTIVE
1	A B **C** D	9/p. 220	Understand a conversation asking about utilities
2	A B **C** D	2/p. 208	Understand a conversation about using bank services wisely
3	A B **C** D	2/p. 208	Use background information on using bank services wisely to understand a conversation
4	A **B** C D	6/p. 215	Understand a conversation about budget expenses
5	**A** B C D	2/p. 208	Understand a conversation about using bank services
6	A **B** C D	9/p. 220	Understand a conversation about budget expenses
7	A **B** C D	8/p. 218	Read utility bills
8	**A** B C D	8/p. 218	Read utility bills
9	A B **C** D	8/p. 218	Read utility bills
10	A **B** C D	8/p. 218	Read utility bills and save money on utilities
11	A B **C** D	3/p. 210	Present real conditional
12	**A** B C D	3/p. 210	Present real conditional
13	A **B** C D	3/p. 210	Present real conditional
14	A **B** C D	3/p. 210	Present real conditional
15	A B **C** D	3/p. 210	Present real conditional
16	A **B** C D	7/p. 216	Future real conditional
17	A B **C** D	7/p. 216	Future real conditional
18	**A** B C D	7/p. 216	Future real conditional
19	A **B** C D	7/p. 216	Future real conditional
20	**A** B C D	7/p. 216	Future real conditional
21	A B **C** D	10/p. 222	Gerunds and infinitives as objects of verbs
22	A **B** C D	10/p. 222	Gerunds and infinitives as objects of verbs
23	**A** B C D	10/p. 222	Gerunds and infinitives as objects of verbs
24	A B **C** D	10/p. 222	Gerunds and infinitives as objects of verbs
25	A **B** C D	10/p. 222	Gerunds and infinitives as objects of verbs
26	A B **C** D	1/p. 206	Vocabulary
27	A **B** C D	1/p. 206	Vocabulary
28	A B C **D**	1/p. 206	Vocabulary
29	**A** B C D	1/p. 206	Vocabulary
30	A B C **D**	4/p. 212	Identify the main idea
31	A B C **D**	4/p. 212	Understand details
32	A B **C** D	4/p. 212	Understand details
33	A **B** C D	4/p. 212	Understand author purpose

Please see reverse for test audio script.

Unit 11 Test Audio Script

Listening I (Tracks 63–64) Page 71.

1. What comes with the apartment?
   M: I'm looking for an apartment downtown.
   F: I have one on Belmont Avenue for $600. It comes with a gas stove.
   M: Are water and gas included in the rent?

   What comes with the apartment?

2. How can you get a cash bonus?
   F: I would like to open a bank account. I understand you have online banking?
   M: Yes, we do. And you can get a cash bonus of $50 if you have direct deposit.
   F: I don't have direct deposit now, but I can sign up for it with my employer.

   How can you get a cash bonus?

Listening II (Tracks 65–66) Page 71.

3. **M:** Hi there. May I help you?
   F: I want to open a bank account. But I have a busy schedule. Are you open late on weeknights or on the weekend?
   M: We're open until 5 P.M. Monday through Friday. On Saturday and Sunday, we're open from 9:00 A.M. until 11:00 A.M.

4. **F:** Can you tell me what you are looking for in an apartment?
   M: We want a one bedroom in Los Altos with a parking space. And we can't spend more than $800 a month plus utilities.
   F: I've got a big one bedroom for $900. It comes with all utilities and free parking.

Listening III (Tracks 67–68) Page 71.

5. **M:** I want to open a bank account. Do you need to see my driver's license?
   F: Yes, or other picture ID. I also need to see a social security card and a utility bill with your address on it.

   Which sentence is true?

6. **F:** I think we should make a budget.
   M: Why? We're paying all our bills on time.
   F: Right, but we need to save more. I'd like to get a car.

   Which sentence is true?

Unit 12 Test Answer Key

	ANSWERS	LESSON/PAGE	OBJECTIVE
1	A **B** C D	2/p. 228	Understand a conversation about favorite places
2	A **B** C D	8/p. 240	Understand a conversation about famous U.S. presidents
3	**A** B C D	2/p. 228	Understand a conversation about the government
4	**A** B C D	2/p. 228	Understand a conversation about favorite places
5	A B **C** D	8/p. 240	Understand a conversation about famous U.S. presidents
6	A B **C** D	8/p. 240	Understand a conversation about famous U.S. presidents
7	**A** B C D	4/p. 232	Read a subway map
8	A B **C** D	4/p. 232	Read a subway map
9	A **B** C D	4/p. 232	Read a subway map
10	A B C **D**	4/p. 232	Read a subway map
11	**A** B C D	3/p. 230	Superlatives: *-est, most, least, one of the most*
12	A B **C** D	3/p. 230	Superlatives: *-est, most, least, one of the most*
13	A B **C** D	3/p. 230	Superlatives: *-est, most, least, one of the most*
14	**A** B C D	3/p. 230	Superlatives: *-est, most, least, one of the most*
15	**A** B C D	3/p. 230	Superlatives: *-est, most, least, one of the most*
16	A B **C** D	6/p. 236	Simple present passive
17	**A** B C D	6/p. 236	Simple present passive
18	A **B** C D	6/p. 236	Simple present passive
19	A **B** C D	6/p. 236	Simple present passive
20	**A** B C D	6/p. 236	Simple present passive
21	A **B** C D	9/p. 242	Past passive
22	**A** B C D	9/p. 242	Past passive
23	A **B** C D	9/p. 242	Past passive
24	**A** B C D	9/p. 242	Past passive
25	A **B** C D	9/p. 242	Past passive
26	A B **C** D	1/p. 226	Vocabulary
27	A **B** C D	1/p. 226	Vocabulary
28	A B **C** D	1/p. 226	Vocabulary
29	**A** B C D	1/p. 226	Vocabulary
30	A B C **D**	7/p. 238	Identify the main idea
31	A **B** C D	7/p. 238	Understand details
32	A B **C** D	7/p. 238	Summarize
33	A **B** C D	7/p. 238	Summarize

Please see reverse for test audio script.

Unit 12 Test Audio Script

Listening I (Tracks 69–70) Page 79.

1. What place is the tour going to see in the morning?
   F: Welcome to Washington. This morning we're going to visit the White House gardens.
   M: When are we going to see the rooms?
   F: We'll do that in the afternoon.

   What place is the tour going to see in the morning?

2. What was President Lincoln most famous for?
   F: Welcome to the Lincoln Memorial Tour. President Lincoln was our 16th president. He is most famous for freeing the slaves during the Civil War.
   M: Was he also the first president killed in office?
   F: That's right.

   What was President Lincoln most famous for?

Listening II (Tracks 71–72) Page 79.

3. **M:** Does the Supreme Court make laws for the country?
   F: No. Congress makes the laws.
   F: Oh, right. So what does the Supreme Court do?

4. **M:** I took my cousin out last night to a new restaurant, but it wasn't that great.
   F: Where do you think is the best place to eat in Washington?
   M: There are a lot of good restaurants. I like Chinatown best.

Listening III (Tracks 73–74) Page 79.

5. **F:** George Washington, the first president, was in office from 1789 to 1797. He is called "the father of our country."
   M: Is that why President Washington is on the dollar bill?

   Which sentence is true?

6. **F:** Thomas Jefferson was our third president. He was elected president in 1801.
   M: How long was he president for?

   Which sentence is true?